Wild Flowers of Britain

Flowers are referred to by their English names in the text. For Latin names see the Index at the back of the book.

OPPOSITE Foxglove *Digitalis purpurea*. One of our largest and most magnificent wild flowers, the Foxglove can grow to a height of five feet in woodland clearings, banks and heaths on acid soil. The long soft flowers bloom progressively up the flower spike, brightly patterned and hairy within, and are pollinated by bees.

ENDPAPERS Blood-drop Emlets *Mimulus luteus* is less common than the closely related Monkey flower, *Mimulus guttatus*, and grows mainly in the north. It can be identified by the large red markings on the petals, for the Monkey Flower is only lightly spotted with red. Both species were introduced from America into Victorian gardens and have spread along the banks of rivers and streams.

Wild Flowers of Britain

SARAH GARLAND

Artus

First published in February 1978 by ARTUS Publishing Company Limited,
11 St John's Hill, London SW11

Printed in Great Britain by Jarrold & Sons Ltd, Norwich

BELOW Viper's Bugloss *Echium vulgare*. The funnel-shaped
flowers of this plant turn from pink to a vivid blue. It likes
a porous, stony soil; here it is flourishing on the top of
cliffs.

PREVIOUS PAGES Honeysuckle *Lonicera periclymenum* climbs
in woods and hedges, twining clockwise round trees and
shrubs with its woody stem. The pale, sweet-scented
flowers with long tubes and abundant nectar are
especially attractive to night-flying moths.

Contents

Introduction

The wild flowers in this book have been grouped under chapter headings according to where they grow. Each plant is seen against its natural background and the influences that shape it: the weather, rich and poor soils, animals and man.

The first chapter tells how warmth-loving plants returned to Britain at the end of the last ice age and how the pattern of plant life has become more and more influenced by the activities of man. The later chapters describe different landscapes and the wild flowers that grow in them, and also some of the ingenious ways in which plants adapt to their surroundings. Answers are given to such questions as why woodland plants flower early and those on a river bank later in the year; how flowers survive on sour inhospitable moorland, shingle beach or rock face, and how a patch of bare earth can be covered so quickly by those plants we call weeds.

The system which is used for classifying plants is explained in Chapter 1, and there is a short note on their reproduction. The few scientific words in the text are explained in the Glossary, and the Index at the end of the book lists all the flowers described.

LEFT Dog Rose *Rosa canina* has flowers which range in colour from white to bright pink. It flowers in June–July, and can be found mainly in hedges and thickets. The hips of the Dog Rose are very rich in Vitamin C, and are most commonly used in jam and syrup.

BELOW Mesembryanthemum or Hottentot Fig *Carpobrotus edulis* is usually magenta with a yellow centre, but sometimes all yellow. It has a long creeping woody stem and stout fleshy leaves. It flowers in May–August on cliffs and dunes.

White Dead-nettle *Lamium album* is unrelated to the Stinging Nettle. Although the leaves are similar it can be identified by its four-sided stem and white hooded flowers. It is perennial and grows on wasteground and waysides.

The classification of wild flowers

Our present system of plant classification is based partly upon a scheme published in the eighteenth century by a Swedish biologist, Carl von Linné (usually called Linnaeus), and partly upon a natural system that has been developed over the years, which groups plants according to their flowers and fruits.

The plants in a standard Flora or book of identification are grouped under the headings of Orders or Families. These are arranged in a sequence that begins with plants which have a simple, primitive flower construction, such as the Buttercups, and leads up to the highly developed Orchids and Lilies. The name of each order usually refers to some characteristic that is shared by the plants within it; for instance the flowers within the order of the Cruciferae or the Cabbage family all have four petals placed crosswise, and those within the order of the Compositae or the Daisy family are compound, with many small flowers growing closely in one flowerhead.

Each order is next divided into groups called genera, and each genus (or group) is further divided into species. The name of genus and species together make up the botanical name of each plant. Taking the familiar White Dead-nettle *Lamium album* as an example, *Lamium* is the generic and *album* the specific name. This genus belongs to the order of the Labiatae, or Thyme family, and the typical features of this family are a labiate or projecting lip, a square stem and opposite leaves. The White Dead-nettle has these general characteristics and another that is less common – the flower has an unusually long throat. It is thus grouped, with several other similar plants, into the genus *Lamium*. This generic name comes from the Greek word for 'throat'. The White Dead-nettle is further distinguished from other plants in the genus by its white flowers and is given the specific name of *album*, which in Latin means white.

It is possible to divide up plants still further into sub-species, and it is at this point that botanists divide themselves into 'lumpers' who are content to deal with species and 'splitters' who will go on separating the flora into micro-species, varieties and forms according to slight differences in the way they are formed.

About one hundred orders are represented in Britain, and some of these contain only one genus or one species. The White Bryony, for instance, is the only member of the Cucumber family in this country, and the Yam family has only one species in Britain, the Black Bryony. The Compositae, or Daisy family, on

8

the other hand, contains at least forty-two genera and well over a hundred species, and is the largest order in the country apart from that of the grasses, the Gramineae.

Sometimes the words 'Monocot.' or 'Dicot.' follow the name of a plant. These abbreviations refer to the two classes into which all flowering plants are divided. The Monocotyledons have only one seed leaf in each embryo and include many soft-stemmed plants with long, often parallel-veined leaves, such as grasses, Bluebells and Orchids. The Dicotyledons, which are the largest group, have two seed leaves to an embryo and include woody and soft-stemmed species.

The origins of scientific plant names are fascinating and diverse, referring to medicinal, domestic and agricultural uses, to myth, legend and superstitions. Many specific names, when translated from the Latin, are a clue to the type of the plant or to where it grows; for example *arvensis* is for plants found on arable land, *sylvatica* for those in woods, *palustris* for marsh plants, *aquatica* for water plants, *perennis* for perennial plants and *communis* for social plants. *Hirsuta* indicates a hairy plant, *vulgaris* a common plant and *millefolium* a plant with many leaves. An example of an individual specific name is *parthenium* for the daisy Feverfew, the herb with which Pericles is supposed to have healed a workman who fell from the Parthenon.

Generic names include *Senecio* from the Latin for 'old man', as a description of the fluffy white then balding seed heads of Groundsel and Ragwort, and *Ononis* and *Onobrychis*, the genera for Restharrow and Sainfoin, both species being eaten by donkeys and deriving from the Greek *onos*, 'ass'. Sometimes a genus is named after a botanist, such as *Lobelia* after the botanist Mathias de L'Obel, and there are several references to Chiron the physician centaur, to Achilles his pupil, and to gods and goddesses such as Adonis, Artemis and Circe.

As the study of botany was bound so closely to that of medicine during the period between Classical and Renaissance times, it is not surprising to find many Latin names referring to the healing properties of plants, e.g. the generic name *Scrophularia* (for the plant which was used to treat scrofula), and the specific name *catharticum* for Purging Flax.

The study of English plant-names is another absorbing subject that can only be referred to briefly in the following chapters. Further reading is suggested in the Bibliography.

Rosebay Willowherb *Epilobium angustifolium* is the showiest of the Willowherbs, with a tall spike of pink flowers.

9

Glossary of terms

corolla

petal

calyx

stamens

leaf

stem

Parts of the plant (buttercup)

Acid: of soil, lacking lime

Alkaline: of soil, containing lime

Annual: a plant with a life cycle of one year

Anther: terminal part of stamen, containing pollen grains

Apomictic: species capable of setting unfertilised seed

Axil: the angle between the stem and leaf stalk

Axillary: growing in an axil

Biennial: a plant with a life cycle of two years, and blossoming during the second year

Boulder clay: clay mixed with boulders as a glacial formation

Bract: modified leaf at the base of a flower

Bulbil: small bulb or tuber

Burr: fruit with hooked spines

Calcicole: a plant characteristic of limy or basic soil

Calcifuge: a plant characteristic of acid or poor soils

Calyx: sepals, forming outer covering of flower

Carboniferous: of soil, producing coal

Chlorophyll: colouring matter of the green parts of plants

Corm: bulb-like underground stem

Corolla: the petals as a whole

Crucifer: flower having four equal-sized petals arranged crosswise

Deciduous: shedding leaves in the autumn

Dicotyledon: plant having two seed leaves to an embryo

Dioecious: having male and female flowers on separate plants

Embryo: rudimentary plant contained in the seed

Endemic: a plant with a habitat in a particular country or district

Ephemeral: of plants, short-lived

Family (*order*): a group of related genera (*see* genus)

Filament: the stalk of the stamen, supporting the anther

Floret: one of the small flowers making up a composite flower

Flush: wet area, usually on hillside, from which water trickles or springs

Frond: a leaf-like organ

Fruit: structure surrounding seed(s)

Genus: group of related species

Germinate: put forth shoots

Habitat: a plant's natural home

Halophyte: a plant which can tolerate a salty environment

Herbal: a book giving descriptions of herbs

Hybrid: an offspring of two different species

Labiate: having a corolla divided into two lip-like parts

Lanceolate: of leaves, long, narrow, as lance head

Maritime: a plant living on the sea coast

Monocotyledon: plant having one seed leaf to an embryo

Mycorhizome: fungal shape taken by the roots of some plants

Order: a group of related genera

Parasite: a plant drawing nourishment from another living organism

Perennial: a plant that lives for more than two years

Pistil: female organ of flower consisting of ovary, style and stigma

Pollen: grains containing male reproductive cells, produced within stamens

Pollinate: place pollen upon stigma or ovule

Pollinium: a structure consisting of a mass of pollen grains, as in Orchids

Rhizome: creeping underground stem producing roots and shoots

Rootstock: underground stem

Saprophyte: a plant drawing nourishment from decayed matter

Sepal: the outer flower parts, together forming the calyx

Spadix: an inflorescence where the flowers are arranged round a thick, fleshy spike

Spathe: the large bract that envelops certain flowers before opening

Species: individual plants bearing certain characters in common

Stamen: male reproductive organ

Stigma: the part of the style that receives the pollen in fertilisation

Style: connection between ovary and stigma

Submaritime: plants usually found within a few miles of the sea coast

Tuber: swollen portion of underground root or stem

Umbel: flowerhead with branches rising from one point, like spokes of an umbrella

Umbelliferous: a plant carrying umbels

Xerophyte: a plant adapted to tolerate dry conditions

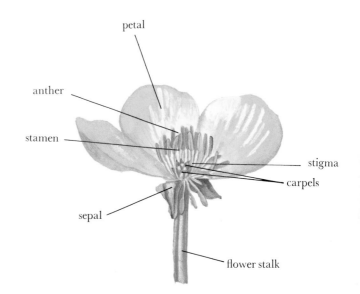

The flower

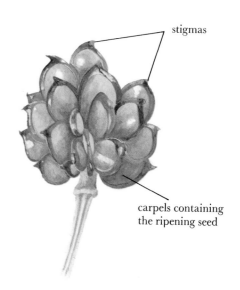

The fruit

11

Basic points about flowers

The long seed pods of Rosebay Willowherb split lengthwise and curl back to release masses of silky-plumed seeds that are carried on the wind.

The different scents, shapes and colours of flowers are all directed towards the production of seed.

The first stage in this process is *pollination*, which occurs when a pollen grain is transferred from stamen to stigma; the pollen grain then produces a tube which grows down inside the tissues of the style and fertilises the female egg, which ripens into a seed.

Some flowers can pollinate themselves. One advantage of *self-pollination* is that the seed is sure to be set quickly, for there is no need to wait for insects or suitable weather for pollination. Many annual weeds are self-pollinating for their success depends upon fast growth; some other flowers are able to pollinate themselves if cross-pollination fails. The disadvantage of self-pollination is that each seed is likely to be an exact image of the single parent plant and so cannot change its shape or habit to suit changing conditions.

When pollen is carried from the stamens of one flower to the stigma of another, the resulting seed is most likely to be healthy and adaptable. Elaborate devices and mechanisms are used by flowers to ensure *cross-pollination*, and some of these devices are described in later chapters.

Pollen is carried from flower to flower by insects, by the wind, or occasionally by water.

Insect-pollinated flowers are generally brightly coloured or scented and may contain sweet nectar. There may be guiding marks upon the petals to direct insects to the nectar, past the pollen which brushes off on their bodies. Sometimes the lip of the flower is shaped to provide a landing stage for bees, flies, wasps, butterflies or moths; the throat of the flower may be short to suit short-tongued flies or bees, or long for the tongue of a night-flying moth.

The flowers of a *wind-pollinated* plant are likely to be less colourful, and to hang swinging freely like those of the Stinging Nettle, or to grow in spikes like those of Sorrel and Plantain, with stamens and stigmas well exposed to the wind. Enormous quantities of pollen must be produced to increase the chance of contact between pollen and stigma, and every sufferer from hay fever knows that many trees and grasses flower in early summer, when clouds of pollen can blow freely on the wind, unobstructed by the later thick foliage.

Whether a flower is pollinated by its own pollen or by pollen

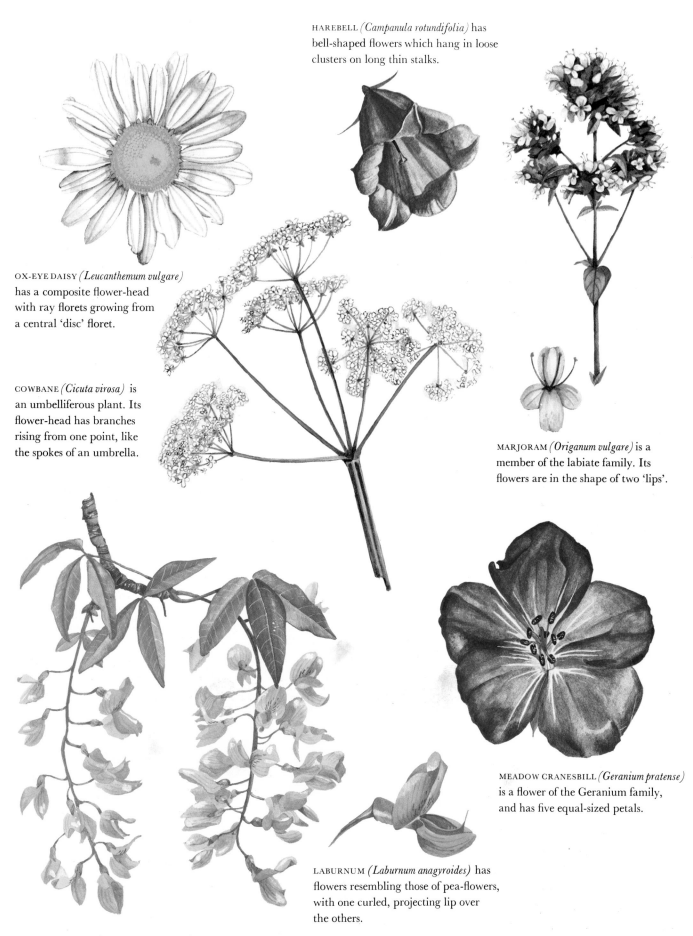

HAREBELL *(Campanula rotundifolia)* has bell-shaped flowers which hang in loose clusters on long thin stalks.

OX-EYE DAISY *(Leucanthemum vulgare)* has a composite flower-head with ray florets growing from a central 'disc' floret.

COWBANE *(Cicuta virosa)* is an umbelliferous plant. Its flower-head has branches rising from one point, like the spokes of an umbrella.

MARJORAM *(Origanum vulgare)* is a member of the labiate family. Its flowers are in the shape of two 'lips'.

MEADOW CRANESBILL *(Geranium pratense)* is a flower of the Geranium family, and has five equal-sized petals.

LABURNUM *(Laburnum anagyroides)* has flowers resembling those of pea-flowers, with one curled, projecting lip over the others.

Some different types of flower-head.
A complete survey is not possible here. These represent only some of the main types.

from another flower, when the egg is fertilised it will ripen into a *seed*. The seed must then be transported for some distance from the parent plant to avoid crowding, and again there are many ingenious ways in which this is done. The wind blows the tiny seeds of Orchids and Heather, and the seeds of Dandelions with their parachutes of silky hairs. Other seeds are hurled from their pods and hooked burrs cling to clothing and the fur of animals. Birds eat juicy berries and deposit seeds in their droppings, and buoyant envelopes of seeds float downstream from water plants.

The embryonic seed is protected by a hard covering, but under suitable conditions of warmth and dampness germination will take place, and the young plant will begin to grow.

Many plants are able to reproduce without seeds by bulbs, corms, creeping stems, tubers and runners. This is called *vegetative reproduction*, and the new plants produced in this way are usually identical to their parent.

ABOVE Eyebright *Euphrasia officinalis* has clearly-marked guidelines and a bright yellow spot to attract pollinating insects.

OPPOSITE The long tongue of a butterfly reaches for nectar down the throat of a lavender flower.

15

1 The History of British Flowers

*T*he latest in the series of great ice ages that have dominated this country began its slow decline about fifteen thousand years ago, and provides a natural point at which to begin a history of the British flora.

Britain had not been entirely covered by the most recent ice-sheet. The glaciers had formed in areas that now have the highest rainfall, in the Scottish Highlands, the Lake District and Snowdonia. Here they had collected, sometimes four thousand feet thick, and from these points the ice had moved slowly east and south, avoiding some mountain peaks, smoothing hilltops, scouring existing river valleys, and finally stopping short at a point south of the Thames. The vegetation covered by the ice died, but in southern England and on mountain-tops and sea cliffs plants of an Arctic type survived, together with some hardy plants that are found on open ground today such as species of Dock, Willow Herb, Plantain and the Sea Campion.

The formation of the ice-sheets had lowered the sea-level probably by about four hundred feet. To the east a broad plain across the North Sea and to the south a land bridge across the Channel connected Britain to the Continent. To the west, England and Ireland were joined across the Irish Sea. Thus, for approximately five thousand years, as the glaciers melted causing the sea-level to slowly rise, plants were able to spread freely from

OPPOSITE Alexanders *Smyrnium olusatrum* is a tall pungent plant which produces yellow flowers from April–June. Its leaves are dark green and glossy, and it thrives on hedge-banks and wasteground near the sea. Here it is growing against the walls of Dover Castle.

BELOW Sea Campion *Silene maritima* is a hardy plant which is common on cliffs and shingle by the sea, and is sometimes found at high altitudes inland. The large flowers grow from tough creeping stalks.

17

Dartmoor was a royal forest in Norman times. The moorland here is bleak and desolate, the chief vegetation being heather.

the warmer Continent into Britain, and it was during this period that our native flora was established.

It is possible to trace how the vegetation began to grow in the raw, bare and often sodden earth, from the evidence in clay sediments and in peat-bogs.

Peat is formed from the partially decayed remains of bog plants and mosses, especially Sphagnum moss. The saturated soil contains no oxygen and this prevents organic matter from decaying properly. Ancient forests, for example, are preserved in peat; a Roman soldier in full uniform has been dug from a Yorkshire bog, and countless millions of variously shaped pollen grains lie in the layers of the peat, as a record of the plant life.

In the levels of peat that were deposited during thousands of years following the melting of the ice, the pollen of Arctic, marsh and weed species is mixed with that of grasses and sedges. In higher, later peat-levels the pollen of birch trees begins to mix with that of larger herbaceous plants, then pine and hazel pollen begins to take over in the south and spread slowly northwards. The climate, which was warmer and drier than it is today favoured the growth of pine trees, and for about two thousand years Britain was almost completely covered by pine forest.

The only areas left for flowering plants that could not grow in the shade of the trees were swamps and marshes, the sea coast, the mountain-tops and a few grassland areas such as one which still exists at Upper Teesdale in Yorkshire. Trees do not grow here because of the height of the land, the high humidity and the generally low temperature. As a result a unique vegetation has been preserved which probably resembles that which covered Britain during the Late-glacial period.

By 5500 BC the climate in Britain had begun to change to the familiar mild and wet weather known as an Atlantic climate. At the same time the steadily rising sea finally covered the last land links with the Continent, and Britain became an island. Plants could no longer spread from the Continent and from this time all new plant and tree species reaching the country were either deliberate or accidental introductions. This has meant that there are fewer species of wild flowers in Britain than in the rest of Europe.

The moist climate encouraged the growth of deciduous trees, and though the pine forests survived in the north of Scotland, they began to be replaced by wych elm, lime and particularly oak over the rest of the country. Alder flourished in the damp valleys, and hazel formed thick underscrub.

During this Early Atlantic period man made little impact upon the environment for both Palaeolithic and Mesolithic man lived by hunting and fishing. However, when Neolithic man settled in Britain in about 3000 BC, bringing with him his sophisticated polished stone axe, his seed grain and his flocks and herds, he took control of the land.

Pollen analysis reveals the early farming methods. To start with, the trees were felled and then burnt so that the land could

Bracken invading grassland. It spreads on to grassland with creeping underground stems and drifting seed spores, and soon overwhelms other plants.

be cultivated, but as soon as the goodness in the soil was used up the farmers moved on and the trees began to grow again. First the pollen of the hazel and the birch appears and then the oak and lime again.

However, when the forest was cleared from uplands and from thin, poor soil, then the change could be permanent. By the end of the Neolithic period some areas in the north-west of Scotland and the Orkneys, parts of Cumberland and some wolds and downs in southern England had been cleared of forest. The trees from Breckland, the East Anglian heath, were cut down and the area was quite closely settled.

After bronze tools replaced the stone axes in about 1700 BC, forests could be cleared more efficiently and the warm, dry weather at this time hindered trees growing in thin soil. It also dried out some low marshlands in Cambridgeshire and Somerset, which were, therefore, inhabited for a while. Then the weather changed back to the wetter, Sub-Atlantic climate which has continued more or less the same up to the present day.

Each time new settlers came to England, some new type of plant seed or fruit would find its way in with them. A collection of plant remains from a Late Bronze Age site in Kent is probably made up of the sweepings from a threshing-floor, and includes flowers, leaves or seeds from the Corn Poppy, Penny Cress, Corn Spurrey, Purging Flax, Silverweed, Hawks-beard and Stinging Nettle. Several of these are thought to have been introduced from southern Europe.

The Iron Age invaders in about 1000 BC had ploughs and knew how to manure the soil so they could establish permanent farms. They also formed a network of villages. Without the trees, plants from the Dock and Daisy families could spread more rapidly and some, such as Fat Hen, Good King Henry, Corn Spurrey and Oat Grass, were used as subsidiary food plants.

An example of an Iron Age meal was found in the stomach of a middle-aged man dug from a Danish peat-bog in 1950. There, in a perfect state of preservation, was a gruel of the roughly ground seeds of Linseed and Barley mixed with seeds of Pale Persicaria, Black Bindweed, Fat Hen, Hemp Nettle, Wild Pansy and Corn Spurrey – a nutritious mixture.

The Romans encouraged the growing of corn, particularly wheat and rye, and drained part of the eastern fenland for the production of wheat. They also introduced numbers of cultivated vegetables and fruit trees – Peas and Radishes; Walnut, Fig and Plum trees; Vines, and many culinary herbs such as Fennel, Dill, Alexanders, and Ground Elder which was eaten as we eat spinach today.

More than six thousand miles of Roman roads were built across the country, providing an ideal environment for the colonisation of plants, for each road was fifteen feet wide and flanked by an open embankment. Many seeds must have been unknowingly transported on feet, clothes, cartwheels and livestock. New species from the Continent were carried back and forth across Britain, mixed with corn and fodder and supplies for the Roman army. The closest recent parallel to such perfect man-made conditions for seed dispersal has been the building of railways and canals in the nineteenth century, during the industrial boom.

Some forests, especially in the Weald of Kent, were felled at this time. The wood was used as charcoal for iron-smelting, an industry which later had a devastating effect upon the forests that remained in medieval times.

The Roman occupation did not greatly affect the pattern of farming in Britain but the Angles and Saxons, who invaded in the fifth century, brought with them great eight-ox ploughs which could turn heavy clay. Lowland forest began to be cleared and the small irregular Celtic fields were enlarged.

During the Anglo-Saxon period, in AD 597, St Augustine landed in Kent, and monasteries began to be built. They became the centres for the development of farming and gardening during the next thousand years.

Herb-gatherers, or Green Men, were familiar figures in Britain. Fragments of their charms, to be chanted as medicines were administered, were recorded by monks, the pagan elements

Red and White Clover *Trifolium pratense* and *Trifolium repens* flourish from May–October and are important protein-rich fodder plants. They are often sown with meadow grass seed or by themselves to produce feed for cattle.

curiously overlaid by Christian censorship. Here, for example, is part of the 'Nine Herbs Charm'.

> 'Thyme and Fennel, a pair great in power,
> The Wise Lord, holy in heaven,
> Wrought these herbs while He hung on the cross;
> He placed and put them in the seven worlds
> To aid all, poor and rich.
> It stands against pain, resists the venom,
> It has power against three and against thirty,
> Against a fiend's hand and against sudden trick,
> Against witchcraft and vile creatures . . .

sing that same charm into the man's mouth and into both his ears and into the wound before he puts on the salve.'

At this time all plants were regarded with deep respect and sometimes with fear. Most species could be used as food or medicine or were thought to have a good or evil influence on people and animals.

The literate monks who managed the vegetable and physic gardens and treated patients in their infirmaries recorded their experiences and discoveries and corresponded with their counterparts on the Continent, often exchanging seeds and cuttings. They studied the *weòds* (the Anglo-Saxon name for small plants, now corrupted to 'weeds'), and *worts* or herbs, and read and translated the Greek and Latin manuscripts on herbs (called 'herbals'), such as the *Herbarium* of Apuleius Platonicus, and the Anglo-Saxon 'Leech Book of Bald', an ancient medical book.

Early Greek writings on plants were reasoned and thoughtful, but did not include a close observation of individual plants. The necessity to differentiate between plants for medicinal purposes led to the first descriptive writings, and laid the basis for later systematic botany.

The *De materia medica* written by Dioscorides in the first century AD gave the names and uses of about five hundred herbs. Although he does not describe many of them in detail, this work remained the authoritative text on the use of plants as medicines for the next fifteen centuries. Most later herbals were based on it to some degree, often mixed with some superstition and magic. One of the most widespread and long-lasting was the ancient sympathetic magic which became the Doctrine of Signatures.

This doctrine supposed that God had left a clue upon the plants he had created, to show how each plant could be used by men as medicines. For instance some yellow-flowered plants could cure jaundice, the little round tubers of the Lesser Celandine or the Knotted Figwort were a treatment for piles, and the red juice and pierced-looking leaves of Perforate St John's Wort would staunch bloody wounds. Even the tiny purple floret that often grows at the centre of the big white flowerhead of the Wild Carrot was used in the treatment of epilepsy, for it suggested the contracted pupil of the eye during a fit.

Common Red Poppy *Papaver rhoeas*. A detailed drawing published by William Curtis in *Flora Londiniensis*, 1797. A hairy annual, with scarlet petals flecked with black at the base, this plant is to be found in arable fields and wasteland, and likes the warmer climate of the south.

After the Norman Conquest forests were preserved by Forest Law for a time as hunting grounds for the aristocracy, but were later given up for farming land. Rabbits, introduced by the Normans, also helped to destroy the forests throughout the Middle Ages so that only remnants of the Royal Forests stand today at Epping, Windsor, the Forest of Dean and the New Forest.

In the twelfth century, the efficient farming methods and sheep-grazing of the Cistercian monks helped clear forests in the more isolated parts of the countryside. The common grazing land that was used by villagers sometimes became rough grass and heathland with a scrub of hawthorn, blackthorn and gorse, a type of vegetation associated with the remaining commons today.

The oak trees were used for shipbuilding. Hazel and chestnut were grown beneath the branches of the oak and their wood was used for iron-smelting. The supply of timber fell so low that stocks had to be imported, and in the mid sixteenth century iron-smelting was forbidden in parts of the country.

The new spirit of enquiry and scientific observation in the mid sixteenth century marked the beginning of the Renaissance in Britain, and the study of plants received a fresh impetus.

William Turner, the Dean of Wells and the 'Father of British Botany' was the first to record his personal findings. Like many of the early botanists, he was a physician. He describes about 240 plants and their localities in his herbal in a careful and detailed fashion. He dismissed the earlier superstitions connected with herbs and their uses, and dedicated his herbal, published finally in 1568, to Queen Elizabeth I.

Much of John Gerard's *Herball*, published in 1597, was copied from a translation of a work by Dodoens, but his style of writing was entertaining and his herbal is still in print today. In his physic garden off Fetter Lane he grew and studied the plants he gathered round London from 'a village hard by London called Knights brige' and from 'Fulham, a Village thereby'. Culpeper's *Herbal* was published fifty years later, and that too is still in print. It was a very popular work, which criticised the methods of qualified doctors and encouraged ordinary people to rely on their own herbal preparations. Culpeper believed that herbs and remedies were dominated and influenced by the sun and the planets, and that the cure is to be found near the cause; an idea which is still evident nowadays when we expect to find a Dock leaf growing near a Stinging Nettle to soothe the sting.

In 1629 the first recorded botanical expedition left London, sailing down the Thames to Kent. It was led by Thomas Johnson, an apothecary, who later edited and improved a new edition of Gerard's *Herball*. The expedition lasted for five days, and they made scientific notes about 250 plants. Several expeditions later Johnson published the first local 'Flora', and then the first two volumes of a Flora of Britain. Sadly he died before finishing this great work. He had recorded seven hundred native British species, one hundred and seventy of them for the first time.

This was a period rich in botanists, each adding their findings to a growing store. The first Professor of Botany was appointed at Oxford, and at about the same time John Ray published his catalogue of plants local to Cambridge. In this work and his later *Synopsis Methodica Stirpium Britannicarum*, published in 1690, Ray described about 970 species, two hundred of which he had noted for the first time during long botanical rides over the British Isles. In this comprehensive British Flora he has sorted through the findings of previous botanists, put them in order and created the beginnings of a system of botanical classification.

Botanical studies fell from fashion during part of the eighteenth century. However the Society of Apothecaries' Garden at Chelsea was established and became a meeting-place for botanists. In 1753 the Swedish botanist, Linnaeus, published a new system of plant classification, of which the structure and nomenclature is still used today.

The 1820s marked the beginning of an enormous increase in the popularity of field botany. The Romantic Revival was under way, and now that the Napoleonic Wars had ended, botanists could travel freely abroad.

Local Floras were published at a tremendous rate. 170 appeared between 1820 and 1880, and Bentham and Hooker published their famous *Handbook of British Flora* which classifies plants according to their natural characteristics and is a standard textbook today. Popular works and 'Familiar Introductions' to botany appeared, such as *Lindley's Ladies' Botany* and *Letters on the Elements of Botany addressed to a Lady*.

Many important plant collections that are still consulted today were begun at this time. One example is the herbarium of George Claridge Druce, who was an Oxford pharmacist and one of the last great nineteenth-century botanists. Druce wrote four county Floras and died in 1932. His herbarium is housed in the Department of Botany at Oxford.

By the early nineteenth century most of the large open fields and commons had been enclosed, changing the appearance of the countryside and the lives of the inhabitants. The nineteenth century also marked the development of industry and the resulting decline in agriculture. Much pastoral land reverted to bracken and scrub, and it was only during the Second World War that land reclamation and arable farming were encouraged once more, a course which has continued, to a lesser extent, to the present day. It is associated with the introduction of modern herbicides and weedkillers, and heavy farm machinery, which have had disastrous effects upon the wild flora.

The sudden demand for home-grown timber during the First World War resulted in the creation of the Forestry Commission, and the conservation of our remaining natural woodlands became a matter of public concern. Signs of the growing awareness of the need to protect our countryside are evident in the increasing numbers of nature reserves, National Parks and local preservation societies, and the more enlightened policies of some farmers and local councils regarding hedges and roadsides.

2 Chalk and Limestone Flowers

*L*imestone is a sedimentary rock that contains at least 50 per cent calcium carbonate, or carbonate of lime. The main ridge of southern limestone crosses England in a broad diagonal from Dorset to Yorkshire, creating a rough steep landscape. The contrasting chalk landscape of the south and south-east is smoothed and rolling, for the chalk is a pure, soft, easily weathered limestone, with a calcium content that can be as high as 98 per cent.

There are many plants that grow almost exclusively on these soils. Some are widely distributed, some limited by climate and temperature to one particular region. They are called *calcicoles*, from the Latin *calx*, meaning 'chalk', and *colo*, 'I inhabit'. The term *calcifuge* is given to those plants that avoid limy soils, from the Latin *fugio*, 'I flee'. Between these two extremes there are many species that can tolerate a variety of soils.

Chalk

Salad Burnet *Poterium sanguisorba* prefers a limy soil. The plants may grow only a few centimetres high on shallow soil but taller and lusher on deeper ground, and the leaflets taste and smell like bitter cucumber. The round heads of green flowers are displaying their red styles. Later, long yellow stamens will hang from the lower flowers and the pollen will be blown by the wind. The related Great Burnet has longer flowers of mahogany red, and grows in damp meadows.

The chalk downs of southern and south-eastern England are formed from marine deposits built up on the sea bed, and later raised by earth movements. The Upper or White Chalk consists of almost pure calcium salt; the Middle and Lower Chalks are more impure and darker coloured; they are generally covered by a soil that is shallow and well drained.

The chalk outcrops of the North and South Downs rise from the sea in the east and meet on the central chalk ridge that becomes Salisbury Plain. From here the broad ridge of Cranborne Chase curves south-west back to the coast, and the Marlborough and Berkshire Downs run north-east from the Plain to the Thames. This forms a natural boundary beyond which lie the wooded Chiltern Hills. They run north to the Cambridgeshire and East Anglian chalk, much of which is covered up with sand and boulder clay. The most northerly chalk outcrop is on the Yorkshire coast. Covering most of the inland chalk of Yorkshire and Lincolnshire is soil originally left by glaciers. The most southerly chalk occurs in a narrow twenty-mile ridge across the Isle of Wight.

The chalk flora is influenced by the thin, dry soil, by exposure to wind and often by the grazing of sheep and rabbits. Many downland areas have been grazed continuously since Neolithic times when the forests were first cleared, and would soon revert to scrub and woodland if the grazing were to cease. This close balance was demonstrated when the rabbit population was

PREVIOUS PAGES The craggy amphitheatre of carboniferous limestone cliffs at Malham Cove in the Yorkshire Dales.

26

struck by myxomatosis; much of the dense, closely bitten turf became coarsened, and seedlings of chalk shrubs such as Dogwood, Spindle and Wayfaring Tree started growing again in many places.

The turf in a well-grazed area is made up of grasses mixed with low-growing or creeping perennial herbs. Many have deep roots to ensure a steady water supply, such as the Salad Burnet. This is a calcicole whose root can grow nearly three feet long, whose flowers are grouped in a round green head, and whose leaves form a rosette pressed flat against the earth, to conserve moisture.

Most of the small downland plants are in flower by June, before the summer drought. The Chalk Milkwort has blossoms of a purer blue than the common species. The flowers are well spaced along a fine stalk, and are each enclosed by two large blue sepals. The Common Rock Rose grows plentifully and has a bright yellow flower, sometimes spotted with orange. Two yellow Vetches form mats over the turf. The flowers of the Kidney Vetch are especially common on sea cliffs and are bunched into two

Rock Rose *Helianthemum chamaecistum*. The bright fragile flowers bloom from May to September, and the creeping plants with their downy leaves are common on chalk and limestone in the south.

27

clumps at the end of each stalk, while those of the more graceful Horseshoe Vetch are fewer, and arranged in a more orderly fashion. The seed pods of the latter are unmistakable, consisting of a series of swollen, crescent-shaped joints, each crescent containing one fertile and one usually infertile seed. Another member of the Pea family is widespread – the Bird's Foot Trefoil, known to children as 'Eggs and Bacon'. It is not confined to chalk but grows, like the Wild Thyme, wherever the grass is short and the conditions are dry.

There are several tiny, fine-stemmed plants that grow unobtrusively among the grasses. One is a partial parasite, the Bastard Toadflax, whose pallid leaves are a sign of its dependence on other plants, for it manufactures little of its own chlorophyll. Two other small species of herbs have been used as medicines: the fierce little annual Purging Flax has a creeping root and minute white flowers raised on a thread-like stalk, and was used as a purgative and laxative. The other is Squinancywort, whose pretty pink, waxy bunches of flowers were once used as a gargle for the quinsy or sore throat. Its leaves, which grow in whorls about the stem, show it to be a small member of the Bedstraw family.

The Eyebright is another partial parasite, though its leaves and flowers are bold and bright. The Large-flowered Chalk Eyebright, one of the many Eyebright species, is a calcicole. It has a dark bushy foliage and complex flowers of white or pale lilac, with converging purple lines on the lobed lips and a single bright yellow spot at the throat to guide the pollinating bees to nectar.

Three members of the Gentian family occur locally over the open downs. The true Gentian is the Felwort or Autumn Gentian, whose flowers are a purplish blue; the Centaury has rose-pink flowers and the Yellow-wort larger, yellow flowers. All these blossoms, on their branched stems, open and close according to the weather, sometimes surprisingly fast, and their leaves have a bitter flavour. The flowers of the Clustered Bellflower, that grows in similar habitats, have been mistaken for Gentians, but they are unstalked, larger, and of a brighter purple than the Gentian.

On the borders of woods and thickets, and in the rough grassland over ancient barrows and along trackways, grow taller and more conspicuous plants. Some of those species that are quite small when growing on the grazed turf grow larger here, and with looser foliage, for example, the Salad Burnet, dark blue Round-headed Rampion and Marjoram. The leaves of the Burnet Saxifrage are similar to those of Salad Burnet but do not have the same scent or delicate flavour, and the flower is umbelliferous. Dropwort is common in some areas, and looks like a large-flowered Meadowsweet. The leaves of Ploughman's Spikenard can be mistaken for a calcifuge, the Foxglove, but they have an aromatic smell; the many flowerheads of yellow and purple are composed of florets and grow from a branched stem.

LEFT Squinancywort *Asperula cynanchica*. A tiny creeping plant found in the turf on open chalk or limestone downs, and occasionally on sand dunes.

RIGHT Field Cow-wheat *Melampyrum arvense* is a rare plant that is occasionally found in cornfields or on chalky banks in the south of England. The long bracts are a bright rose pink, and the flowers yellow-throated.

BELOW Deadly Nightshade *Atropa belladonna* grows in woods and scrubby places on alkaline soil. The dusky purple bell-shaped flowers are followed by glossy black berries, and all parts of this perennial bushy plant are extremely poisonous. Some creatures seem able to eat the leaves with impunity, and the leaves on this plant have been nibbled by caterpillars.

Like the Foxglove it is a biennial, germinating in the spring, wintering as leaves, and flowering the following year.

In June and July two species of Scabious flower abundantly on chalk. The Field Scabious is common and bears single mauve flowers made up of florets, packed into a convex shape; the Lesser Scabious has a flatter and paler flower and a shorter stalk. Tough-stemmed Knapweeds flower at the same time. There is the stout Black Knapweed with fine purple petals growing from a dark knobby clump of bracts, and the Great Knapweed which has paler bracts, larger flowers and grows taller.

An overgrown chalk quarry is the most likely place to find the Deadly Nightshade, which will sometimes grow here to a height of five or six feet, shaded by Dogwood and Privet bushes and festoons of Traveller's Joy. A purple stem rises from the perennial root and branches into a bush with dark green, hairless leaves. The purple-brown flowers bloom from June to September, growing singly and developing into a smooth black berry which can tempt children because it is juicy and sweet. The whole plant is highly poisonous; the roots are the most powerful, then the flowers' leaves and then the berries. This is the reason for its generic name of *Atropa*, for Atropos was the Fate who wielded the shears to cut the thread of human life. The specific name of *belladonna* is thought to refer to its use in the sixteenth century as a juice to enlarge and thus beautify the pupil of the eye, a use that

29

was put to good purpose in Victorian times when it was found to be very helpful in eye operations.

The calcium content in the chalk rock is soluble and can be gradually washed away by rain. This can result in surprising patches of acid heathland on the summits of chalky downs and hills. As the rainfall is light on these chalk downs, this happens more slowly than in the west, where the limestone is often washed away in many places. Occasionally deposits of sand or gravel have covered the flatter chalk hilltops, and can produce a similar result. Heather and Heath Bedstraw grow here and since they avoid chalky soil it is a good sign that the soil is acid.

From Cambridgeshire northwards the chalk becomes buried deeper and deeper beneath glacial deposits. In the area known as Breckland it is covered by sand and by boulder clay in much of Suffolk, Norfolk, Lincolnshire and Yorkshire. The clay often contains lime and consists of a crushed mixture of rocks carried south by glaciers. The Oxlip is the most famous species to grow on this clay, and should not be confused with the hybrids that sometimes occur elsewhere between the Cowslip and Primrose.

The chalkland flora described is remarkably constant over the downs and differs only in its regional rarities. For instance the Tall Broomrape, a two-foot pale yellow parasite on Knapweed, grows frequently on Salisbury Plain. The Isle of Wight is one of the few places where the Purple Cow-wheat grows – a dramatic plant with pink and yellow flowers and long, finely divided pink bracts – and on a few escarpments in the Chiltern Hills grows the annual Candytuft. This plant is also often cultivated in gardens.

There is a group of highly developed and often extraordinary-looking plants that are especially associated with chalk and limestone – the Orchid family.

The majority of British orchids grow on chalk grasslands and the North Downs are particularly rich in rare species. Apart from their general preference for calcareous soils, the warmth and dryness of the limestone, and the unploughed turf suit many orchids, whose slow development and uncertain germination require a stable environment.

There are at least fifty orchid species in this country, each with a fascinating and complex life cycle. The Bee Orchid, a widely distributed species, is a good example.

The Bee Orchid produces an average of ten thousand seeds from each seed pod, and though this may sound a very large number, it is necessary to make sure the plant will reproduce. Each seed is minute, like a grain of dust, and as it is only released in dry weather, it can be carried for long distances on the wind. The size of the seed means that it can be easily dispersed but also that it does not hold much food to help it grow. This difficulty is overcome at an early stage in germination when most orchids become infected by a fungus that is present in the soil. The two then generally develop together, each providing food for the other. The Bee Orchid is most dependent upon the fungus during the early period of its life, as it develops underground as a

OPPOSITE Oxlip *Primula elatior* grows in only a small area in East Anglia, where a limy clay covers the chalk. It is growing here with Sanicle in a coppiced wood. The cluster of flowers is similar to those of the Cowslip, but are much larger and of a deeper yellow.

31

structure called a 'mycorhizome', producing a leaf during the first year and a first tuber a year later. Many other orchids spend longer as a mycorhizome; the Burnt Orchid for instance, will spend ten to fifteen years in this way before producing a leaf. When the tuber finally appears, the mycorhizome withers and the fungi remain in the roots.

The Bee Orchid now sends up a small shoot that grows larger each year, and also leaves that live throughout the winter, unlike those of most other orchids, whose leaves die down. It develops two large tubers for food storage, one shrinking as it provides food for the growth of the plant, the other plumping out with further food supplies. Sometimes a tuber will produce a bud which will develop into a separate aerial stem. Finally the plant grows strong enough to flower, and a flower spike grows six to fifteen inches tall, producing two to seven blossoms. These have spreading pink

Bee Orchid *Ophrys apifera* is widely distributed about the country, preferring a limy soil and a short turf. The dramatic flowers with their pronounced, patterned lip appear in June and are self-pollinating.

Lizard Orchid *Himantoglossum hircinum* is one of the rarest and strangest of the British orchids, and is found mainly on chalk in southern England. The long twisting lip of each flower is clearly shown, and its goat-like smell appears to attract pollinating flies.

sepals veined with green, rolled rich brown petals, and a big soft, gently pouched lip of the same colour, marked with paler patterns. The pollen grains are, in common with those of most other orchids, grouped into heavy masses consisting of thousands of grains, known as pollinia. There is often a sticky disc on this structure, so that it will manage to attach itself to the head of a pollinating insect. The Bee Orchid, however, usually pollinates itself.

Other species in this orchid genus of *Ophrys* are pollinated by 'pseudo-copulation'. This occurs when a male insect hatches earlier than the female and, treating the orchid lip as a mate, flies onto it and goes through the motions of copulation, during which he removes the pollinia. In the case of the Fly Orchid for instance, the insect which assists in this way is the male burrowing wasp, for the lip of the Fly Orchid resembles the female of the species. When the female wasps hatch, the male loses interest in the flower, and this may be one reason for the rarity of the Fly Orchid, for few seeds can be set. It is possible that there has been a type of female bee that is now extinct, but which looked like the lip of the Bee Orchid, and that pollination originally occurred in this way. But self-pollination appears to work well for the Bee Orchid, which grows on lime soils throughout England and Wales, although it does mean that abnormalities go on being reproduced.

There are many variations upon this cycle among the Orchid family, for instance the Bee Orchid dies after flowering once, whereas many orchids flower for several successive years. Also the plants have developed many different ways of encouraging insect pollination. It is sometimes possible to guess at the type of insect that pollinates a species by examining the length of the flower's spur; those with a short spur are likely to be pollinated by the short-tongued bee, while those with a long spur are adapted to the proboscis of a butterfly or moth.

The substance stored in the orchid tuber has been used as a human food for thousands of years. It is highly concentrated and nourishing. For example, one ounce of the dried powdered root, dissolved in boiling water, was considered sufficient to feed a seaman for a day when rations were short during a long voyage.

The three most widespread orchids are the Common Spotted, the Early Purple and the Pyramidal Orchids. They are most often to be found growing in large numbers in the south but sometimes grow as far north as Scotland, usually on soils containing lime. The South and especially the North Downs are the places to find some of our rarest and strangest orchids. The Man Orchid grows here, and the rare Monkey and Military Orchids, whose dangling curved and patterned lips almost look like arms and legs. The Lizard Orchid is perhaps the most dramatic of them all; from the pale green and purple, goat-smelling flowers, tumbles a twisting lip, spotted with red and two inches long. Happily this type of orchid seems to be increasing in quantity, although it is still a rare species.

Limestone

The plant life in limestone areas can differ from that in chalky soil, partly because there is less calcium in limestone, but mainly because there is more rain and a higher humidity in the west.

In Somerset the Mendip Hills are formed on a ridge of hard and old carboniferous limestone. In many places it is covered up by acid soil, but where the rock is exposed in steep cliffs and gullies Yew and Ash trees grow, and below them Red Valerian, Stonecrops and Wall Pennywort. The Cheddar Gorge provides a typical example of this rugged limestone landscape, and here the Cheddar Pink still grows high up on rocky ledges. Other rare plants on the cliffs include the Small Meadow-rue and Cut-leaved Self-heal, which is similar to the common species, but has white flowers and divided leaves.

Botanists have studied and written about the flora on the limestone cliffs of the Avon Gorge for the last five hundred years and many of the rare plants are still there. For instance the Honewort, which was found there by William Turner on one of his botanical trips in the early sixteenth century, grows there today. The Bristol Rock Cress flowers in May, the big red open flowers of Bloody Cranesbill bloom in June, and in July the brilliant blue Western Spiked Speedwell flowers from cracks and crevices. The scrambling Madder grows over the rocks. It is the largest member of the Bedstraw family.

There are further outcrops of carboniferous limestone in the wooded Wye Valley, in parts of Pembrokeshire and on the

Marjoram *Origanum vulgare* grows in large perennial clumps on dry banks, but becomes less common towards the north. The pink flowers often bloom with yellow Lady's Bedstraw and blue Meadow Cranesbill along the roadsides in chalk or limestone country. The aromatic leaves are used as a flavouring herb.

Gower Peninsula, where the rare little Yellow Whitlow Grass grows up the sea cliffs. It is a crucifer with a hairy circle of leaves and bright yellow flowers. Inland there are outcrops among the Brecon Beacons, and to the north a magnificent stretch of limestone country, across Anglesey and at Great Orme's Head. Here maritime plants such as the Vernal Squill and Scurvy Grass are mixed with the calcicolous Kidney Vetch, Rock Rose, Bloody Cranesbill and the early-flowering Hairy Violet.

Smoother and more recently formed limestone (known as 'Jurassic') is found in the area between Bath and north Oxfordshire, including the Cotswold Hills.

Across these grow many of the calcicoles that inhabit the chalk downs. Among the long grass on the roadsides grows the blue-flowered Meadow Cranesbill, Purple Milk-vetch, Dark Mullein, Lady's Bedstraw, Crosswort and Marjoram. The big Woolly Thistle, the Bee Orchid and a slightly different variety, the Wasp Orchid, grow on rough grassland, and in some Gloucestershire beech woods grows the ghostly pale Downy Woundwort and the even rarer Red Helleborine.

Two other rare plants grow on the Cotswold limestone. The Perfoliate Penny-cress is well known to botanists, but is easy to overlook, for it is an ordinary plant that looks like a stunted Field Penny-cress. The other, by contrast, is one of the loveliest of British wild flowers, the Pasque Flower. It grows on chalky turf in East Anglia, on downs and in some parts of the Cotswolds. Its name means 'Easter flower' and was so called by Gerard because it flowers at Easter. The short hairy stem grows up from feathery silky leaves, and carries a richly purple flower with a mass of golden anthers at its centre.

North of Oxfordshire, in Lincolnshire, Rutland and Northamptonshire, the land is mostly used for farming and the limestone is covered in patches by soil carried there by the glaciers. Therefore abandoned limestone quarries are probably the most hopeful place to find limestone plants. Further north, in the North Riding of Yorkshire, there is a last outcrop of the smoother type of limestone, which stretches from the coast at Scarborough to the escarpments which border the moorland all around Rievaulx Abbey.

Many of the plants growing on similar soil in the south also grow here – Kidney Vetch, Salad Burnet and Deadly Nightshade for instance – but some are quite rare or do not grow here at all, such as Traveller's Joy, Yellow-wort and Dark Mullein. These are replaced by northern plants such as Wild Columbine, Herb Christopher and Lady's Mantle. The yellow Common Rock Rose is joined by the rarer White Rock Rose, and the Meadow Cranesbill of southern limestone is replaced by the smaller, mauver flowers of the Wood Cranesbill, *Geranium sylvaticum*.

A narrow strip of yellow magnesian limestone runs north from Nottingham. It is softer and newer than the carboniferous and occurs at a lower altitude, so it is the most northerly station for many southern limestone plants.

Pasque Flower *Pulsatilla vulgaris*. This beautiful little flower with its richly purple sepals backed by silky hairs and with a boss of golden anthers has suffered from the ploughing of much of our downland and is now only found in a few scattered places across the south and south east of England.

35

The Derbyshire Dales to the west mark the first outcrops of northern carboniferous limestone, and the wild and dramatic scenery of crag, scar and scree begins. It is a high tableland deeply cut by fast-running streams and the rivers Dove and Derwent. Yew, holly and a few ash trees grow from the cliffs, and the vegetation includes many northern plants.

Across the flat tops of the rocks the high rainfall has caused heavy leaching, and acid heathland is common here. It is on the steeper and more exposed limestone that more various northern plants will be found: the big yellow Globe Flower, the paler yellow and purple Mountain Pansy, the Giant Bellflower, and the uncommon Spring Cinquefoil grow well in these conditions.

The largest exposed area of carboniferous limestone in Britain begins fifty miles to the north and extends over much of Yorkshire. Although there is further limestone country in Westmorland, Cumberland, Northumberland and parts of Scotland, much of it is underneath a different type of soil and where it does break through it contains a flora similar to that on Yorkshire limestone.

Limestone 'pavements' are found in this area. The heavy rain has worn through the joints in the rock forming deep cracks. Soil collects in the cracks and then seeds begin to grow. They are well protected from the weather and from animals, so that often rare plants can survive.

One of the most beautiful northern plants grows in damp places on the limestone – the Bird's-eye Primrose. In shape it resembles a small, fine Oxlip, but it has pale mauve upright flowers, each with a yellow eye, and the leaves have a silvery underside. With luck the Lady's Slipper Orchid still survives somewhere among the rocks or scrubby woods. It was first identified in 1640 in an Ingleborough wood, but two hundred years later it had become very rare. The large flower has a big pouched yellow lip, and purple petals and sepals. It is cleverly formed so that small bees are guided to the nectar on the 'slipper' floor, and then out by a separate exit to ensure cross-pollination. Other insects are sometimes trapped in the slipper, and sometimes a bee will lie there during the night, apparently sheltering from the weather.

The limestone area round Upper Teesdale has been mentioned in an earlier chapter, for typical plants have grown there since Late-glacial times. Hoary Rock Rose and Shrubby Cinquefoil grow on the granulated 'sugar' limestone that outcrops on the high ground. High limestone meadows are the place to find Lesser Valerian, Alpine Bartsia and a large species of Lady's Mantle. The Teesdale Sandwort and Teesdale Violet are found in this area, and on damper ground grow Bird's-eye Primrose, deep blue Spring Gentians and the Scottish Asphodel. On the crags and scars the maritime Thrift and Sea Plantain are mixed with Mountain Avens and Alpine Meadow Rue, characteristic of the mountain flora that is considered in a later chapter.

ABOVE Giant Bellflower *Campanula latifolia* grows mainly in the north and can reach a height of five feet in damp, semi-shaded places. The long purplish-blue flowers open progressively up the leafy stalk.

OPPOSITE Globe Flower *Trollius europaeus* grows in damp grassy places, in the north.

BELOW Bird's eye Primrose *Primula farinosa* is a northern Primrose, whose delicate yellow-eyed flowers grow in a cluster from a single stalk. It grows on open, damp ground.

3 Arable and Wasteground Flowers

ABOVE Shepherd's Purse *Capsella bursa pastoris*. The purse-like shape of the fruit gives its name to this familiar small plant which grows on sandy, loamy and gravel soil.

BELOW Common Field Speedwell *Veronica persica* was introduced into Britain less than two hundred years ago, but is now one of the most widespread of the many Speedwell species. It grows on disturbed ground and is a common garden weed. All Speedwells have four petals with clear guidelines for insects, and two prominent stamens.

Arable land

Included under this heading are the familiar field and garden weeds which are the first to grow on newly dug ground and are so difficult to get rid of. Plants such as Groundsel and Chickweed do not live long but will reproduce very fast, while longer-living plants such as Coltsfoot and Dandelion possess deep persistent roots. The names given to such plants show their effects upon farmers and gardeners. The Dodder has been called 'Hellbind', 'Strangleweed' and 'Beggarweed' and the Restharrow names like 'Stayplough', 'Sitfast' and 'Poverty'. 'Land Robber' is an old name for the Dock and 'Ground-swallower' the original Saxon name for Groundsel.

Two common plants provide examples of typical weed characteristics. One is the Shepherd's Purse, a little plant with a brief, intense life cycle. The size of the plant varies according to its situation, from an inch to eighteen inches high. The flowers are self-pollinated before they open, and each plant soon produces about three thousand seeds, which are released gradually over some weeks. The seeds are slightly sticky and are carried away in mud on boots and shoes, on car tyres and birds' feet. They are also eaten by birds, horses and cattle and are distributed in their dung. This process warms and soften the coating of the seed so that it may begin to grow more quickly. If the seeds fall on hostile ground they can remain dormant for thirty five years or more until conditions improve. If they land on favourable ground they will grow quickly and can sometimes produce ripe fruits within six weeks, so that three generations can succeed each other during one year. It is a tough plant which can live and flower throughout the winter. The Chinese grow it especially to eat as a spicy vegetable. Other plants with a similar, brief life cycle include Chickweed, Speedwell, Groundsel and Red Dead-nettle.

The Field Bindweed, also known as 'Devil's Guts', grows well for different reasons. As every gardener knows, it is a perennial, and grows a network of white, fleshy roots which are almost impossible to destroy. One flower produces about four seeds which are comparatively large and heavy. Although this means that they are not carried far, it does mean that the growing plant has a good food supply. As the seedling develops, the roots begin to grow and can cover as much as thirty square yards in a season. They have been found growing twenty-three feet underground and can be cut to pieces by spade or plough, each piece sprouting and growing again, so that cultivation of the land can actually encourage the weed. The delicate white, or pink and white trumpet flowers are sweet-scented and visited by insects during the day. At night, or during damp weather, the flower folds its pleated petal and closes with a twist. Other perennials that can reproduce from small pieces of root or stem include Coltsfoot, Ground Elder, Dock and Dandelion.

A high proportion of the seeds accidentally introduced during the past five thousand years have belonged to plants that grow on bare open ground and are well suited to farmland and wasteland.

The most common way for seeds to be accidentally carried about is in the sack of seed corn. Until the invention of the seed-drill the seed was sown by hand, hoeing was ineffective, and weeds grew with the corn. On the threshing-floor seeds similar in weight and size to the corn grains, or small enough to slip through the corn-riddle, could survive, to be sown again with the seed corn or ground with the grain at the mill. Sometimes the results could be disastrous, certain cornfield weeds such as Darnel Grass, Corn Marigold or Corncockle being toxic and thus poisoning the flour. The increased purity of modern seed corn has meant that these weeds are seldom mixed with a crop today, but some, such as the bright yellow Corn Marigold, can still be found on sandy soil as a weed in a market garden, or on the borders of a field of corn stubble.

The red, white and blue of Corn Poppy, Mayweed and Cornflower dominated many cornfields until the introduction of chemical weedkillers. The Corn Poppy is the most prolific. One seed-head holds fifteen hundred to three thousand seeds, and these can stay in the soil for at least a hundred years, ready to flower when the soil is disturbed and the seed brought to the surface. An experiment in one arable field showed that there were 113 million dormant Poppy seeds per acre. (There were also 68 million dormant seeds of other weed species present.) Sometimes a mass of Poppies will spring up when downland is ploughed or when earth is turned for roadworks or building sites, and there is the historic example of the Poppies in Flanders that covered trenches and shell holes during the First World War.

Poppy seeds have a high germination rate, but even in ideal conditions the seeds do not all begin to grow at once but do so gradually over at least eight months. This process is known as 'natural dormancy', and is a common feature of many annual arable weeds, as a further insurance for survival.

Of the four most common Mayweeds or Chamomiles, the Scentless Mayweed is the most abundant, and the Stinking Mayweed the most unpleasant. Wild Chamomile looks similar but is faintly scented. The true Chamomile, a sweet-smelling and perennial plant, which was used for Chamomile lawns in Elizabethan times, and another variety for Chamomile tea and medicines, are less common.

The pollen of the blue Cornflower has been found in soil of the

Field Bindweed *Convolvulus arvensis*. The delicate flowers with their faint, sweet scent belong to one of our most persistent perennial weeds. It is found throughout the country on cultivated or waste ground, and on sand dunes.

PREVIOUS PAGES A Hampshire cornfield in July.

41

ABOVE Prickly Poppy *Papaver argemone* mingles with Corn Poppy *Papaver rhoeas*. Prickly Poppy is pale scarlet with numerous bristles and flowers in May–July. OPPOSITE ABOVE Corn Poppy is deep scarlet and flowers in June–October. It is common in the south but becomes scarce towards the north of Britain. The fragile petalled flowers last only for a day and possess no nectar; they are pollinated by flies, beetles and bees that visit the flower for the pollen food.

OPPOSITE BELOW Scarlet Pimpernel *Anagallis arvensis*. A little creeping annual, square stemmed, with fresh shiny leaves and flowers that open and close according to the weather – hence its country name of Poor Man's Weatherglass. It grows on bare or disturbed ground, in arable fields and on sand dunes.

Late-glacial period, but the open arable fields later gave it an ideal place in which to grow. Now the flower is rarely seen growing wild, but is cultivated in gardens.

As already mentioned, the seed-drill, invented by Jethro Tull in the early eighteenth century, was one of the first ways of controlling weeds. The next came in the nineteenth century when the threshing-machine was invented. The machine was much more efficient than hand threshing, so only a few seeds would escape with the grain.

Another nineteenth-century innovation meant that the number of weeds growing in damp fields, such as the Mousetail, was soon reduced. This was the improvement in the draining of farmland, and also the fact that the water-table became lower when enormous quantities of water were piped off to the

expanding cities and industrial areas.

New methods for screening and sorting seeds, and the passing of the Seeds Act in 1920, meant that seed grain became purer. Then, in the 1940s, the first chemical herbicides were introduced and selective weedkillers began to be developed. Not only did this mean that there were fewer weeds in crops but also that with chemical fertilisers fields could be used all the time, and that consequently there were fewer fallow periods when weeds could grow.

There are still many farms where the land is allowed to rest, and weedkillers are restricted. In these fields it is possible to gain some idea of how rich and varied the flowers in the old cornfields were. Listed below are some of the plants found flowering among the stubble in a Suffolk field in October. They are short or creeping, having avoided the reaper.

The daisy flowers of Wild and Scentless Chamomiles; pale yellow Wild Radish; Fluellen with fine creeping stem and tiny purple and yellow snapdragon flowers; the larger pouched bright pink flowers of the Lesser Snapdragon; Scarlet Pimpernel; pale mauve Field Woundwort; Black Nightshade with curving white petals; Field Pansy, sometimes known as 'Look-up-and-kiss-me'; the tiny brilliantly blue flowers and large bristly leaves of Lesser Bugloss, and the lighter, streaked blue of Speedwell. Among them the Corn Marigold shone yellow. Though it had been beheaded by the reaper, it had grown again from the lower stalk and was already distributing its seed.

Knotgrass *Polygonum aviculare*. A tough, creeping, many-branched plant that is common on bare ground, paths and roadsides. The small insignificant flowers bloom from June to November and it is related to the Persicaria, Dock and other common weeds.

Wasteground

Plants that are common on the newly turned soil of arable fields also grow well on open wasteland, such as the Speedwell, Scarlet Pimpernel and Fumitory, with its finely divided, pale grey leaves and delicate purple flowers. The Pink and Pale Persicarias, Yellow Toadflax, and Black Medick with little yellow flowerheads and clusters of round black seed pods, may blossom for a season or two, before the larger and more competitive plants and grasses take over.

Some species of the larger Goosefoots are often among the first colonisers. They will cover a bare, newly dug embankment or heap of builders' rubble with their angular spreading branches, tight spikes of flowers and massed green, brown or black seeds. Fat Hen is one of the most common, with leaves which are long and narrow (lanceolate) or toothed. The leaves of the Common Orache may look slightly mealy, and there are several similar Goosefoots with red stems and leaves. Close to the ground the Common Knotgrass can form a dense mat of tough spreading stems, dotted with minute pink flowers. It is often covered with dust and mud on the edge of a road and survives the constant crushing of boots on footpaths. It is also known as 'Blackstrap', 'Clutch' and 'Ironweed', and its generic name, *Polygonum*, means 'many-jointed', a reference to the long-jointed stems.

A surprising variety of plants will grow on rubbish dumps. Unusual species may appear, their seeds falling from the stuffing of broken furniture, from among kitchen waste or old packing material. Foreign species may grow in quantities on the wasteground near dockyards, having been imported with cargoes from abroad. Wool is especially suitable for transporting seeds; 348 species from such seeds have been recorded as growing at Tweedside, and a wool waste known as 'Grey Shoddy' that is sold as a manure for market gardens will sometimes produce unexpected results. Exotic plants, such as Hemp, may grow round chicken runs, and others sprout from the bird seed that is scattered on garden lawns. Usually these foreign plants flower briefly, then wither without setting seed, but sometimes conditions are suitable and they settle permanently.

One unwelcome example has been the Hoary or Thanet Cress. The seeds are thought to have been brought to England mixed with the hay stuffing of mattresses bearing wounded soldiers in 1809. The soldiers were landed at Ramsgate and a local farmer ploughed the mattress stuffing into his fields at Thanet. The Cress appeared with his crop, thrived and began to spread over southern England, and continues to spread north and west today. The plant develops at a tremendous speed. Within nine weeks a seedling can grow a twenty-one inch vertical root. Shallow side roots grow horizontally from the parent stem and soon produce new shoots, and roots that curve down to a depth of ten or twelve feet. The plant can cover large areas but fortunately it does not produce seeds as quickly as it grows.

A member of the Borage family, Amsinckia, which appears to have arrived with poultry seed from California, is an example of a recently arrived weed species that is growing well in this country. Known in America as 'Yellow Forget-me-not', the large, rough-leaved plant with hairy stem and curving spike of orange or yellow flowers has spread from a Suffolk poultry run across the rubbish tips and sandy fields of East Anglia.

Plants that were once grown in the early physic gardens are now found on old rubbish tips, dumps and wasteland. The seeds were probably transported with the rubbish or on the tyres of lorries, or were disturbed from dormancy. The seeds of the Henbane, for example, can remain dormant for at least a hundred years, which may explain the erratic and unexpected appearances of the plant.

The Henbane is a member of the Nightshade family, the Solanaceae, an order that includes the Potato, Tomato, Tobacco, and the poisonous Belladonna or Deadly Nightshade. Henbane, too, is highly poisonous. It was used medically as a narcotic and to soothe tooth and ear ache. The flowers are striking, of a faded pale yellow veined with purple, and with a dark purple centre. The flowers grow in a double row up the curved stalk and later develop into dry bell-like capsules, each of which contains about three hundred seeds. The leaves and stalk are covered with sticky glandular hairs which smell faintly unpleasant. This wasteground plant used to be common but is now becoming rare.

Motherwort, a herb that was used to help women in child-birth, has become a rare plant of waste places, though when seen it is unmistakable, standing two to four feet high with dark green, deeply cut foliage and bright pink labiate flowers. Two other members of the Labiate family grow in similar places and by waysides; the Black Horehound with rings of darkly purple flowers and an unpleasant smell, that was used for treating dog bites, and the White Horehound. The latter has a pleasant smell, rings of white flowers, and both leaves and stem are covered in a dense white down. It is a native plant which has also been grown in gardens for many hundreds of years. It was brewed as beer or tea or given as a syrup for coughs, a practice that is still followed in parts of the country today.

Three other plants that were taken from the countryside to be grown in gardens but are now found again in waste places are the Knotted Figwort, the Wormwood and Mugwort. Wormwood and Mugwort both belong to the genus *Artemisia* and are very

Rosebay Willowherb *Epilobium angustifolium* can grow to a height of eight feet and the spikes of pink flowers bloom from June to September. Although it reproduces abundantly by seed, it also spreads vegetatively by creeping stems and will form large colonies in woodland clearings, railway embankments and waste ground.

ABOVE Henbane *Hyoscyamus niger* is found on bare or disturbed ground, sometimes on rubbish tips or by the sea. The strange dull yellow flowers are clearly veined and followed by bell-shaped capsules that contain poisonous seeds.

bitter; Wormwood was used to expel worms and Mugwort to flavour ale. Knotted Figwort was used to treat the scabby disease of Scrofula, hence the generic name of *Scrophularia*.

The plant population is ever-changing. Sometimes a plant will appear and will spread widely, then slowly die out over a long period. Sometimes a plant such as the London Rocket will arrive, flourish and vanish within a very short space of time. This cruciferous plant spread in multitudes over the charred remains of London after the Great Fire of 1666, then, as suddenly, became extremely rare.

The Rosebay Willow-herb and Oxford Ragwort have suddenly thrived during the last hundred years, and for similar reasons. They both need wind to spread their seeds and are happy on open and burnt ground, so the new cindery railway embankments of the nineteenth century provided an ideal place for them and passing trains blew their seeds the length and breadth of England.

Their origins are quite different. The Rosebay Willow-herb has been recorded as a Late-glacial plant, but was seldom seen until the nineteenth century, when it began to spread slowly along railway tracks, then more and more quickly during the twentieth century, over scorched heath and woodland and on the bombed sites of the Second World War.

Oxford Ragwort comes from Sicily, from the very slopes of Etna, so it was well adapted to ashy railway lines. A specimen of the plant was sent to Linnaeus at the Oxford Botanic Garden at the end of the eighteenth century. It began to grow there and on some of the Oxford walls, beginning to spread with the arrival of the railway. It joined the Rosebay Willow-herb on the bombed sites together with another foreigner, the Chinese Buddleia.

OPPOSITE Oxford Ragwort *Senecio squalidus* likes walls and wasteground, often beside railway lines. The scientific name of the genus *Senecio* refers to the white hairy seed-heads.

46

ABOVE Wall Pennywort or Navelwort *Umbilicus rupestris*. The leaves are dimpled and grow from walls and rocks down the western peninsula.

ABOVE Wild Wallflower *Cheiranthus cheiri* is a tall and fragrant perennial which flourishes by old walls and in dry, limestone rocks.

ABOVE Ivy-leaved Toadflax *Cymbalaria muralis* hangs and trails over walls in town and country. The little snapdragon flowers bloom during frost-free months.

Stone walls

The flora on stone walls will often include the tough hardy plants that grow on wasteground and in dry fields, such as the Cats Ears, Hawkweeds and Hawkbits, and the softer-leaved, milk-tinged Wall Lettuce. All these grow flat rosettes of leaves to prevent the moisture from draining away into the stony soil. They send taproots deep into cracks and often develop into miniature plants an inch or two in diameter when conditions are bad.

Whitlow Grasses and Little Cresses with rings of leaves, such as the common Hairy Bittercress and Hairy Rock-cress, grow among mosses and lichens. They blossom in good weather and have four white flower petals set crosswise.

The succulent Stonecrops that are now so typical of stone walls grow naturally on rocks, cliffs and shingle. They spread in mats with creeping, rooting stems, and they sometimes fall in curtains, with their star-shaped flowers opening to show clustered stamens. The Wall Pepper is the most familiar species, with little fat, rounded, hot-tasting leaves and yellow flowers. The white-flowered English Stonecrop is widespread, and in Wales and the south-west of England the Rock Stonecrop, a rarer species, has a tall flower stalk that ends in a cluster of yellow flowers. Another species from the Stonecrop family that grows mainly in the south-west is the Wall Pennywort, that has a spike of pale, greenish flowers, like miniature Foxgloves, and round, shining leaves. Like the other wall plants they vary in size, growing from two inches to nearly two feet in height.

Three plants which originally came from other countries are now common on our walls. The Wallflower, with yellow or orange flowers, also grows on cliffs and railway cuttings. Red Valerian, Red Betty or Soldier's Pride was a garden plant in the early seventeenth century. By the nineteenth century it grew well in railway cuttings, and it is now common on walls and rocks in the south and west. The big straggling plants with their long smooth leaves grow from cracks between bricks or stones. The clustered flowers are generally red, but occasionally pink or white. Its less common relative, the true medicinal Valerian, is found in ditches and damp places.

The third plant, the Ivy-leaved Toadflax, was first recorded in 1617. This plant produces a hanging curtain of shiny leaves and tiny, mauve, snapdragon-like flowers, which bend towards the light and are pollinated by bees. They flower from May to November, and as the petals are shed and the seeds form, the

stalk turns from the light and leans back to drop its black seeds against the wall.

It is interesting to compare the plants on stone walls in the north, west and south-west of the country. The thin mosses, Cresses and Yellow Welsh Poppies of the hilly districts in Cumbria and Wales gradually change to a thicker vegetation in the Midlands. Down the south-western peninsula, as the climate becomes milder, the walls are increasingly covered until, in Cornwall, the stones disappear under a blanket of grass and herbs, of Creeping Thyme, Stonecrops, Saxifrages, Speedwells, Primroses, Violets and Foxgloves.

Red Valerian *Centranthus ruber*. Originally a garden escape, it is now common in the south on walls, cliffs, quarries and steep banks. The clustered red, pink or white flowers blossom for half the year and the leaves are smooth with a greyish bloom.

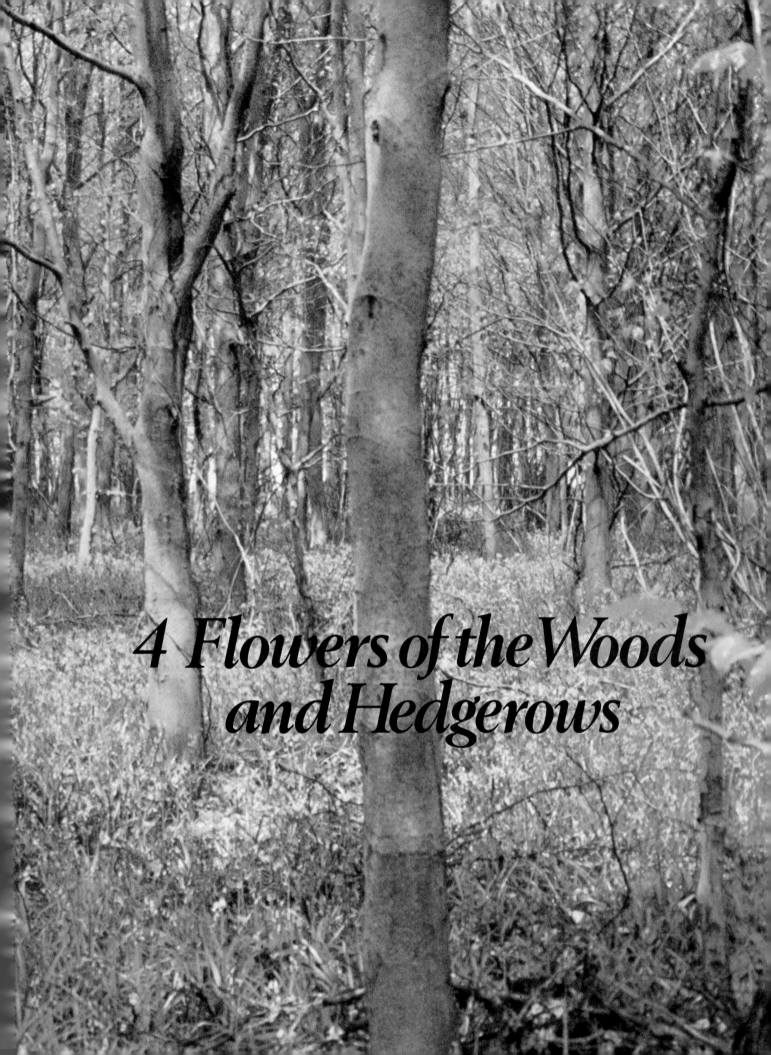

4 *Flowers of the Woods and Hedgerows*

Lesser Celandine *Ranunculus ficaria*. The burnished pointed petals of the Lesser Celandine in woods and shady hedge-banks are among the earliest, most welcome signs of spring. It can reproduce rapidly by means of the small tubers that grow among the roots and can become a persistent weed in a shady garden.

*T*he natural vegetation over most of the British Isles is woodland, and if it were not constantly checked by man the dense forests that covered the countryside five thousand years ago would soon return. The progression of plant life towards woodland can be seen everywhere, in a neglected garden, ungrazed downland, or an overgrown ditch.

The damp British climate suits deciduous trees, particularly the oak. On chalk and southern limestone there are many beech trees. At high altitudes and in the north of Scotland most trees are of pine or birch.

The greatest problem for woodland plants is that they do not get enough light. Most plants have solved this by flowering, fruiting and manufacturing food as early in the year as possible, before the canopy of leaves is formed overhead and the sunlight reduced to a dappled shade. This is the reason for the drifts of Bluebells, Anemones and Lesser Celandines that flower in March and April, whose leaves have withered by June, and whose bulbs, tubers or roots lie swollen with food until the spring.

Some plants may be unable to flower at all if the shade becomes too dense. They grow just leaves for several years on end, and only flower if a branch or a tree falls and lets in the sunlight. The ground that is cleared of hazel coppice in the autumn is likely to be covered by a carpet of Violets and Primroses in the spring and later with Bugle, Foxgloves, Red Campion and St

John's Wort. As they cannot be sure of flowering every year, most woodland plants are perennial and many are able to reproduce vegetatively as well as by seed. The large colonies of Bluebells, Lesser Celandines, Dog's Mercury and Stinging Nettles grow from bulbs, tubers or creeping underground roots and stems.

The distinguished botanist, Sir Edward Salisbury, noticed the large size of the seeds and fruits produced by woodland flora, and concluded that the necessity for a good supply of food for the developing seedling attempting to gain a place among the dense woodland vegetation was especially important. The disadvantages, such as the necessarily limited numbers of seeds produced by the parent plant and the difficulties of distributing heavy seed, are outweighed by the advantages.

One common way in which woodland seeds are carried is by ants. The large seeds of plants such as the Spurges, Hellebores, Dead-nettles and Annual Mercury, have oily parts that attract ants and snails. An ant will carry the seed off to its nest, eat the oil and drop off the seed; a snail will eat the oil and leave the seed somewhere along its slimy trail. A study of this method of transport showed that seeds were often carried from forty to two hundred feet from the parent plant.

Oakwoods

Fragments of the ancient oakwoods remain, such as those in Windsor Forest, the New Forest, Sherwood Forest and the Wychwood Forest in Oxfordshire. Otherwise our oakwoods have been planted or greatly changed, and are often used as cover for fox and pheasant.

Of the two native species, the common or pedunculate oak, whose acorns grow on stalks, is the most widespread, and the durmast oak, whose acorns are stalkless, will grow in a sandy, acid soil. The oakwood flora is rich and varied, as the roots of the oak tree grow deep into the soil, leaving the food near the surface for the plants, and the oak leaves soon rot to provide a rich humus.

One of the first woodland plants to flower is the Dog's Mercury. It comes up as a green loop from among the leaf litter, doubled over to protect its growing point, and straightens out to open pairs of fresh green leaves and spikes of yellow-green petalless flowers. The creeping underground stems weave a dense mat close under the soil.

Following the Dog's Mercury, two members of the Buttercup family flower in shady places from February to March. The

Lesser Celandine has glossy leaves and flowers, the pointed petals burnished yellow, with honey sacs for insects. However, there are few insects at work so early in the year, and when the flowers are not fertilised they cannot produce seed, so they use another method of reproduction. Little round bulbils grow on the unfertilised plant, in the axil or joining-place of the upper leaves. In the early summer these bulbils loosen and fall to the ground, where they can grow into a new plant. The Celandine can also reproduce from the tubers that grow among the underground roots. The Wood Anemone, or Windflower, also reproduces by creeping roots. The pale, uplifted petals droop and close at night or during wet weather.

By April most of the shady woodland plants are in flower. There is only a little time left before the trees finally shut out the sun. Bluebells flower in masses on light soil, the Primrose on richer loams, and the strange Oxlip, with its head of dark Primrose blossoms, on boulder clay in eastern England. On dry soils the scented white bells of Lily of the Valley will sometimes spread under the trees. In damper woods another member of the Lily family will open similar broad leaves, but it can soon be recognised by its smell as a Ramsons, a wild Garlic whose white, sharp-petalled flowers are grouped at the top of each stem.

There are at least five Violets that are native to Britain, and two hundred in various places throughout the world. The flowers make nectar for bees, but our climate is often too cold for bees in early spring, and the flowers are seldom pollinated. The Violet, like the Celandine, has had to find another way to produce seed. It does so by flowering for a second time, in the autumn. Unlike the purple or white, often delicately scented flowers of the spring, these autumnal flowers are hidden away among the leaves. They are self-pollinating, have no petals and no smell, but produce many seeds. The most common Violets are the Dog Violet and the Wood Violet, both of which are scentless.

Wood Sorrel also grows small, self-pollinating flowers in addition to its spring flowers of white, finely veined with purple. The leaves consist of three fresh green leaflets which are affected by changes in the light or bad weather, when they fold neatly downwards and protect their delicate surfaces. Three local names illustrate different aspects of the plant. Woodsour is one, for the leaves contain oxalic acid and taste fresh and sharp. Alleluya is another, for it flowers at Easter. A third is Cuckoo's Meat, for the plant's food supply is stored in little swollen structures which are edible and grow at the base of the leaves. Despite its name, the Wood Sorrel is not related to the field Sorrels or Docks.

The Toothwort, which is a parasite, flowers early, but it looks as much like a fungus as a flower. Its pale pink, fleshy spike of flowers grows close against the trunk of a tree, usually a hazel or elder tree, and feeds from its roots.

By June, most plants have finished flowering in the deep wood, and only the leaves remain. The leaves of Wood Sorrel, Dog's

ABOVE Wild Garlic or Ramsons *Allium ursinum*, a pungent white plant with leaves like those of Lily of the Valley, is to be found in woodland and thickets, liking a porous soil, rich in humus.

LEFT Wood Sorrel *Oxalis acetosella* is one of the few plants that can grow and blossom in shady woodland. The pale, delicately veined flowers appear in April and the sensitive sharp-tasting leaves can remain green throughout the year.

Mercury, Barren Strawberry, Brambles and Nettles border paths and rides. However, two plants carry on flowering in the summer, despite the shade. The first is Enchanter's Nightshade with its bare little spike of pinkish-white flowers and broad, pointed leaves, and the second is one of the commonest woodland species, the Ground Ivy. It has kidney-shaped leaves which grow from long runners, and dark blue flowers growing in loose circles among them. The bitter leaves were used for clearing and flavouring ale in medieval times, and Alehoof is its country name.

Beechwoods

Stinking Hellebore or Bear's-foot *Helleborus foetidus* has bell-shaped flowers which droop in clusters from a thick stem. It thrives mainly in the limy soil of dry woodland and scrub.

Unlike the oakwood just described, the floor of a beechwood may be partly covered with Ivy or Brambles, or be quite bare of plants. The smooth, pale beech trunks rise from a deep layer of beech leaves, that take longer to rot down to humus than the leaves of oak. The dense roof of beech leaves casts a deep shade, and the roots lie close under the thin soil, taking the food that could be used by herbaceous plants.

Beech trees in the south of England grow on soil that is unsuitable for the oak, on shallow chalk and limestone, and sometimes on sand and gravel on top of chalk, so beechwoods occur most frequently on the North and South Downs, the Chiltern Hills and the Cotswolds. Sometimes yew trees grow among them, creating an even denser shade.

Two plants typical of beechwoods have adapted to the shade in a similar way. They are saprophytes, which means they get their food from decaying matter with the help of a fungus, instead of from the sunlight. One is the Yellow Bird's-nest, a strangely naked-looking plant that grows up from the dead beech leaves, without any colour. The other is the Bird's Nest Orchid, which has pale yellowish-brown flowers growing in a spike from the scaly stem. This plant follows the pattern of many orchids, spending nine years gathering energy to flower, then often dying at the end of one flowering season. Another saprophytic orchid, which was first discovered in 1842, is so rarely seen that it is sometimes thought to be extinct. It is perhaps the rarest of the British flowers, the Spurred Coral-root. It lives underground as a rhizome (or underground stem) together with its fungus, and flowers after about ten years, needing continually damp conditions to survive. When at last the flower spike appears between May and September, the stem is pink and the few big flowers pale yellow, with a large pink-spotted lip.

When the beech trees are young or widely spaced, and the sunlight can reach the woodland floor, more plants grow. Many woodland orchids grow in beechwoods, as most orchids like a limy soil. The Twayblade and Broadleaved Helleborine are common. The Large White Helleborine, an orchid of southern beechwoods, grows from six to eighteen inches high, with handsome white flowers alternating up the stalk. The rarer Red Helleborine is sometimes seen in Cotswold beechwoods, and may grow. as leaves for many years as it waits for enough light to enable it to flower. Fifteen flowers may grow from a stem, each a bright rose-pink with a pink-tipped white lip.

Two Hellebores are among the earliest flowering plants on chalk and limestone in the south. The two species, the Green and the Stinking, are both close relatives of the cultivated Christmas Rose. The flowers have five green sepals; those of the Stinking Hellebore are numerous, pink-edged and drooping, those of the Green Hellebore uplifted and plain. The petals are difficult to find and consist of small tubes filled with nectar. All the Hellebores are poisonous, but have been used as medicines in small quantities.

Herb Paris grows on damp limestone. It is another uncommon species and is easy to overlook. It is a 'Herb of equal parts', for there are four leaves circling the stem, four sepals, four greeny-yellow petals, eight stamens and later one black, shiny, poisonous berry in the centre. The flower of the Moschatel or Town Hall Clock may also seem unassuming from a distance, small and pale green on its long stalk, but look closer and see the five flowers pressed close together, gazing north, south, east and west, and the fifth straight upwards to the sky.

A common plant in glades and half-shaded woodland on alkaline soil is the Sweet Woodruff. It is a member of the Bedstraw family and has the usual clambering stem with rings of little pointed leaves growing from it and small white flowers. The whole plant is sweet-scented, and the scent becomes stronger as it dries, so it has been used for stuffing mattresses, for hanging in clothes cupboards and for laying between the sheets in the linen-press.

Sweet Woodruff *Galium odoratum*. The pure white starry flowers bloom in April and May in shady places. When dried the whole plant smells sweetly of newly-mown hay.

Ashwoods

Ash often grows on southern chalk and limestone, but is soon shaded out by the beeches that develop. Further north where there are fewer beech trees, the ash becomes the natural woodland on some shallow limestone soils.

Rocky screes, valley sides and limestone pavements in Derbyshire and Yorkshire are ideal ground for natural ashwoods. The soil must be shallow, for if it reaches any depth then oaks will take over. The well-spaced leaves of the ash, and the limestone soil, suit many herbaceous plants.

Some plants which grow in limy soil in the south such as Traveller's Joy and Honeysuckle are uncommon, but there are several other plants that are only to be found on the shady northern limestone. The Globeflower grows in damp ashwoods, two feet high with a hollow branched stem and each branch topped by a big, yellow, buttercup-like flower. Jacob's Ladder is commonly seen in gardens, but grows wild in rocky northern woods. The flowers are bright blue with drooping yellow stamens, and the leaflets grow up the stalk in pairs. Baneberry, or Herb Christopher, is a rare plant that is found mainly on Yorkshire limestone. The leaves, roots and shining black berries are all extremely poisonous; the spikes of white flowers appear in June. Toads appear to be attracted by the putrid smell of the plant, and Toadroot is a local name.

Pinewoods

The Pine grows well on light sandy soils, and on heath and moorland. It is most common in the north of Scotland where the oak and beech do not grow.

Vegetation beneath the pines is sparse, and may consist of patches of Heather, Bearberry, Crowberry and Bilberry. Between them grow a few acid-loving herbaceous plants such as Tormentil and Heath Bedstraw.

Some species grow especially well in northern pinewoods and nowhere else, such as the Chickweed Wintergreen which is unrelated to the Chickweeds or Wintergreens, but a member of the Primrose family. The delicate white, drooping flower rises from a high ring of leaves and reproduces by creeping underground stems. The true Wintergreens possess five species that all prefer the pinewoods, but can sometimes be found on stable sand-dunes. Their beautiful waxy pink or white flowers hang from a short stem, and a long style often sticks out from the flower cup.

One orchid which lives on decaying matter, with a similar life cycle to those already described, occurs in the Scottish pinewoods. This is the Coral-root. It is different from the Spurred Coral-root because it produces a small amount of its own chlorophyll, which gives it a greenish tinge. The stem is short and

LEFT Jacob's Ladder *Polemonium caeruleum* has flowers which grow in a purplish-blue cluster from June–August. It is a rare plant of grassy places and open woods in the north.

the flowers a pale yellow. Two other Orchids grow here: the Creeping Lady's Tresses, whose white flowers twist in a spiral up the stalk, and the Lesser Twayblade, a little Orchid with reddish flowers, that often grows from a tuft of moss, hidden beneath a Heather clump.

The southern pinewoods on the sandy commons of Surrey are of fairly recent origin, and the vegetation there is mainly composed of heathland plants.

Hedgerows

BELOW Primrose *Primula vulgaris*. The delicate yellow flowers, growing singly on narrow hairy stalks, are a common sight in hedge-banks and shaded grassland in early spring.

The plants described so far have all been those that grow deep within woods. There is another group that grow well in dappled shade, on the borders of woodlands and thickets, and in hedges.

Some of our most ancient hedges are likely to be the remnants of original forests, left as field and parish boundaries by the Celts and Saxons.

The majority of our hedges were planted in the eighteenth century, when the open farming system that had been practised since Anglo-Saxon times was brought to an end, and the land enclosed. Within the last twenty years a fifth of the 800,000 kilometres of British hedges have been destroyed as fields have been enlarged.

There is no sharp definition between the flora of hedge and roadside, but the species described below are those that generally do not like direct sunlight. They can be roughly divided into three groups: the woody climbers, scrambling plants and some shade-loving species.

Many of these smaller plants such as Violets and Lesser Celandines also occur in woodlands, and flower early before being shaded over. One of the first to flower is the Primrose, the *prima rosa* of medieval Latin, the first sign of spring.

The pale yellow flowers are delicately constructed to ensure cross-pollination, for each plant bears either 'pin-eyed' or 'thrum-eyed' flowers. The stigma in the pin-eyed flower shows clearly at the centre of the blossom, the anthers being out of sight down the tube, while the stigma in the thrum-eyed flower is hidden, and five anthers are displayed. Visiting bees and moths, which go deep inside for nectar, thus brush pollen from thrum-eyed anthers onto pin-eyed stigma, and vice versa.

Another typical, early-flowering hedge plant is Jack-by-the-Hedge, or Hedge Garlic. It grows straight and tall, the flowers are pure white, the leaves are wide, toothed, and a fresh bright green.

RIGHT Wild Arum *Arum maculatum*. A broad, pale green hood encloses the flowers of the Arum, and these are positioned male above female below the club-shaped, purplish spadix. The glossy arrow-shaped leaves appear in early spring and are sometimes spotted with purple; the flowers bloom in April and May; in autumn the poisonous bright orange berries ripen.

The distinctive Wild Arum has many names; it is called 'Cuckoo-pint', 'Lords and Ladies', 'Dead-man's Fingers', 'Parson in the Pulpit' or 'Parson's Billycock'. A wide, pale green leaf called a spathe encloses the spadix, which is swollen and purple at the tip. Lower down the spadix and wrapped about by the spathe are groups of primitive flowers. The upper group consists of a ring of downward-pointing hairs, the next group produce the pollen, and the lowest group are female flowers that produce the fruits. Flies are attracted by the foetid smell of the plant, crawl past the hairs and are thus trapped, to wander aimlessly about, covering themselves with pollen and pollinating the female flowers until all are fertilised. Then the hairs finally wither, and any insects still alive can escape.

As the flowers die down, the dark green, often purple-blotched leaves remain, covered by the summer hedge vegetation. In the autumn the surrounding undergrowth dies down and the plant is revealed again, the lower group of flowers now changed into a stocky head of poisonous orange berries. The thick bulbous root is also poisonous.

In early summer many plants grow towards the light. Greater Stitchwort, which has large white starry flowers, and Greater Chickweed with similar smaller flowers, lean upon each other with their long weak stalks. Sticky Goosegrass climbs up the hedge and attaches itself with little hooks to nearby plants and to all who pass by. It is a member of the Bedstraw family, and is much liked by geese. Another Bedstraw, the Crosswort, with rings of tiny yellow flowers, tangles with Purple Bush Vetch against the hedge shrubs.

The tall Red Campion of the shade will often mix with the White Campion that grows in the open to produce a pink flower.

LEFT Red Campion *Silene dioica* grows in semi-shady places and among tall grasses. It often hybridises with the White Campion and produces pale pink and lilac flowers of varying shapes and shades.

Traveller's Joy *Clematis vitalba* climbs vigorously over shrubs and hedges. The pale greenish-yellow flowers are followed by seeds with long grey plumes for wind distribution, giving it the alternative name of Old Man's Beard.

The more local Betony has rich purple flowers.

In the hedge itself grows Honeysuckle, its tube filled with sweet nectar that is drunk by long-tongued moths. Some insects snip the tube and steal the nectar, bypassing the pollen. Woody Nightshade or Bittersweet, although it is not a climber, can grow high into a hedge. The petals of its purple flowers curl back to reveal a tight spike of yellow anthers. The berries ripen through every shade from green to yellow, orange and red, and are poisonous.

Hops and Traveller's Joy are two climbers that rarely grow north of Yorkshire, and prefer a limy soil. Hops are not as common as Traveller's Joy, but they are very persistent, with a tough stem growing from a perennial rootstock. The male and female flowers grow on separate plants, and it is the dry scaly flowers of the females that have been used in the brewing of beer since the Middle Ages.

They provoked considerable controversy when they were first introduced as an ingredient, supplanting the old ale flavourings such as Ground Ivy, Mugwort and Woodruff, and both Henry VI and Henry VIII legislated against the use of Hops. John Evelyn, as late as 1670, was writing that the Hop 'preserves the drink indeed, but repays the pleasure in tormenting diseases and a shorter life'.

Traveller's Joy has a fibrous stem which can grow six inches

thick and will loop from tree to tree. The foliage can smother and smooth the outline of a hedge for miles beside the road. In the autumn the pale green flowers develop into the familiar plumed fruits of Old Man's Beard.

The two Bryonies are unrelated to each other. They can easily be told apart, as the Black Bryony twines clockwise, and has shiny heart-shaped leaves, while the White Bryony climbs with the aid of many long curling tendrils and has paler, vine-shaped leaves. The root of the Black Bryony is large and has a black skin and yellow flesh, but the White Bryony's pale root can grow very large. The berries and roots of both Bryonies are highly poisonous.

Black Bryony *Tamus communis* is a perennial climber with dark green heart-shaped leaves. Its flowers, which appear in May–August, are yellow-green, and its berries are red and poisonous.

63

5 Grassland and Roadside Flowers

Spear Thistle *Cirsium vulgare* may grow five feet tall with fiercely spiny leaves, bracts and sharp 'wings'. It is the most common of the large Thistles, and is widespread throughout the country.

PREVIOUS PAGES Meadow Buttercup *Ranunculus acris* flowers in abundance from April to October in meadows and damp grassy places. It is not grazed by cattle and therefore forms 'islands' of golden yellow in meadows and pastures.

Grassland

The rough, uncultivated grasslands of heath, down and moorland are described in other chapters; the grasslands referred to here are those enclosed meadows and pastures that form so much of the countryside.

There is less of a division between pasture and meadowland than there used to be, as many fields are now both mown and grazed in one season. However, in general, pastures are grazed and the plants which grow there are less varied than those in the meadows, where the flowers are undisturbed until hay harvest.

Grass was recognised as a crop and became an established part of crop rotation in the eighteenth century, when the best grass seeds began to be saved. Children were employed to gather ripe seed heads from certain grasses growing in fields and hedgerows, which were then sown the following year. Now there are fewer permanent pastures, the sown grasslands are known as 'leys', and grass seed mixtures can be carefully controlled and varied for a hay or forage crop.

Seeds of red and white Clovers are usually put into these mixtures because they add protein to the grass, they help to bind the turf together and they put nitrogen back into the soil. Some farmers sow small quantities of the seeds of such edible herbs as Yarrow, Burnet, Ribwort Plantain and Chicory, either mixed with their grass seed or sown as a pure 'herb strip' across a ley. These plants are all rich in certain minerals and are much liked by cattle and sheep. Otherwise herbaceous plants are kept out as far as possible, partly because they take up good grazing land and partly because some are harmful to livestock.

Thistles are typical grassland weeds. The leaves of the Spear Thistle grow in a large spiny rosette, smothering the surrounding grasses. The stem will grow up to five feet tall and the single flowerheads are large and purple. This is one of the most common thistles, but there are at least thirteen other species in Britain, ranging from the Melancholy Thistle that is most common in Scotland, to the Nodding Thistle that grows mainly on chalk and limestone. The Creeping Thistle is particularly difficult to get rid of and can spread very rapidly.

The common Broad or Round-leaved Dock is another grassland plant avoided by sheep and cattle, and usually surrounded by coarse, uneaten grass. The closely related Sorrels, however, are often eaten by stock and were widely used as a potherb in this country before the introduction of the broader-leaved

66

Bulbous buttercup *Ranunculus bulbosus* is very similar to the Meadow Buttercup except that the sepals are turned downwards, and it is less deeply lobed. It flowers in March–June on dry grassland and roadside verges.

Fritillary *Fritillaria meleagris*. The single, nodding flowers are generally a pale or dusky pink, chequered with a darker pattern, and occasionally completely white. The narrow grey stem and leaves merge with the grass in water meadows, but it is sadly an uncommon plant and survives mainly in protected fields in the south of England.

ABOVE Meadow saffron *Colchicum autumnale* has a pale rosy mauve flower which is crocus-like in shape. Its leaves are bright green – appearing in spring and dying before the flower appears in August–September.

French Sorrel. Both the small, narrow-leaved Sheep's Sorrel that grows on poor soils, and the larger Common Sorrel, have freshly acid-tasting leaves.

If Ragwort is growing it often indicates that the soil is poor or shallow. It is a large, strong perennial plant, with yellow daisy flowers. It is often found in a rabbit warren since rabbits do not like it and it does not mind the droughty conditions. It is poisonous to cattle and sheep, either when fresh or when dried with hay.

Another, but less violent, poison is present in the three most common Buttercups, the Meadow, the Creeping and the Bulbous. These all have an acrid and bitter taste, but become quite harmless when dried in hay. The Ox-eye Daisy has acrid but harmless leaves, and grows in meadows and along grassy embankments across Europe and parts of Asia. The stems are tough and wiry, similar to those of the Scabious and Knapweed and other summer-flowering grassland plants.

Three parasitic species grow as weeds on grassland. The Dodder is a complete parasite that begins to grow and root normally, then twines its red, thread-like stem round a host plant, attaches itself, abandons its roots and draws all its food from its

Cuckoo Flower *Cardamine pratensis* has sweetly scented flowers whose colour may vary from white through pale to dark lilac. It grows in the long grass of damp meadows or marshes and is visited by bees and butterflies.

host. Bunches of tiny pink flowers blossom up the leafless stems. Each species of Dodder grows on a different plant, such as Furze, Thyme, Nettles or, most commonly, Clover.

The Lesser Broomrape, another parasite, is a fleshy purple and yellow, and attaches itself to Clover roots. Its many tiny seeds will float unaided for miles on the wind. The Yellow Rattle or Hayrattle draws nourishment from grass roots and grows about a foot high. It can be recognised by the large, flattened, pale green sepals that almost enclose each yellow flower, and by the rattling of the seeds in their dry pods as they are shaken in the wind.

Grassland flora will vary widely according to the type of soil, the temperature and the rainfall. A high moisture content in the soil is particularly important for the growth of rich grasses, and more grass is grown in the west and south-west of the country than in the drier east.

From the seventeenth century until recent times low-lying fields have been deliberately flooded by changing the course of rivers or streams during the winter months. This was done in order to fertilise the ground with rich silt. It still happens naturally today when water runs high. These fields are too damp for grazing and are mown for hay, which means that a greater variety of plants can grow there.

One of the most famous, yet most uncommon flowers of damp meadows is the Fritillary, *Fritillaria meleagris*. It grows mainly in Oxfordshire and some other southern counties, and is so beautiful and strange that the flowers have been mercilessly picked. They now only survive in protected places, such as the Magdalen College Meadow at Oxford. The plant grows from a tiny bulb in late March, has a few narrow leaves, a twelve-inch stem and a single drooping flower, occasionally white, but usually chequered minutely with pink and purple. The Latin name derives from *fritillus* or 'dice-box', and *meleagris*, 'guinea fowl', both being references to the patterned petals.

Another bulbous plant found in similar places is the Wild Daffodil, which still grows wild in Gloucestershire and the south-west.

Meadow Saffron or Naked Ladies, the *Colchicum autumnale*, grows locally in damp fields. The lanceolate leaves appear in the spring, together with the fruits. By autumn the leaves have died and the flowers open, single, pink and palely naked, like a Crocus flower. Although it is a deadly poison, the corm has been used in small doses as a treatment for gout since the earliest times, and is included in the British Pharmacopoeia today.

The plants of low-lying water-meadows are similar to those found on river banks and in marshland or wet ditches. Many of them are lush tall species that attract pollinating insects with their sweet smells. The familiar Cuckoo Flower, Milkmaid or Lady's Smock, is a delicately scented, pale mauve-flowered perennial that blooms early in April. Another is the Meadow-sweet, with its mass of creamy blossoms and almost over-sweet scent. It flowers from June to September. The Ragged Robin has

69

a more subtle scent which attracts butterflies and moths. It is related to the Red Campion but grows on moister ground and has deeply divided petals and a fine dark stem. The leaves of the Water Mint, crushed underfoot, produce a familiar scent in damp places. This is the most common of our wild mints. The flowers are pale lilac, crowded into rounded tufted heads, and appear late in the summer.

Roadsides

Daisy *Bellis perennis*. Often flowering throughout the year, the Daisy must be the most familiar of all our wild flowers, only disapproved of by those who wish a perfect lawn.

Although chemicals have been used extensively in the past to kill roadside plants, many local councils are now changing their policy and avoid spraying grass verges and banks. Field weeds and garden escapes grow among native plants.

The plants closest to the road edge either grow low or along the ground, for they are most frequently cut and trampled. Among them grow several species from the genus *Potentilla*, whose name comes from the Latin *potens*, meaning 'powerful', and refers to their use as medicine. The easiest of these to find is the Silverweed because of its soft, bright, silvery leaves. The single flowers are yellow and the swollen root has been used as a food in times of famine. Cinquefoil has similar yellow flowers but, as its name suggests, the leaves are divided into five leaflets, and these were used to cool fevers and agues. The plant spreads by runners, like the closely related Wild Strawberry, and the stem can grow for five feet from the original root. The Tormentil has smaller yellow flowers and leaflets in groups of three, and is most common on acid soil. It can grow tall on pastureland, but a creeping form is most common on roadsides. Its name refers to its former use as a treatment for relieving the torments of colic and diarrhoea.

The Daisy, the 'Day's Eye', is the flower of lawns and other trodden places. It has acrid leaves and flowers that have been woven into chains for centuries and celebrated by poets from Chaucer to Wordsworth and Keats.

The Pineapple Weed or Rayless Mayweed is also from the Daisy family, but has a different history. It was first recorded growing in Wales in 1871. It probably came from the Pacific coast of North America, and became common in the early twentieth century. The ribbed fruits stick to muddy feet and car tyres and are, therefore, carried a long way. The divided leaves have a strongly pungent smell, similar to that of some other Chamomile and Mayweed species, and will still grow after they have been trampled down.

OPPOSITE Silverweed *Potentilla anserina*, seen here against a watery background, has distinctive silvery pinnate leaves that border footpaths and other bare ground and spread quickly by creeping runners. The solitary flowers bloom in midsummer. Like many Potentillas the Silverweed is a tough plant and can withstand trampling.

Yarrow *Achillea millefolium* has strong, downy stems, aromatic and finely-divided narrow leaves and a head of flowers that are usually white but occasionally pink, lilac or purple. It is a common roadside plant and can survive in hostile conditions as can the related Chamomiles and the Pineapple Weed.

OPPOSITE Common Mallow *Malva sylvestris* is a common plant of roadsides and waste places, although it becomes scarcer towards the north. The pinkish-purple, dark-veined flowers bloom from June throughout the summer. Like several other Mallow species it appears to grow well in drought conditions.

Three species of Plantain have been common trackway plants for thousands of years. They are all very adaptable, the leaves growing large in long grass and smaller and tougher on a trodden path. The common Broad-leaved Plantain or Waybread is one of our most ancient medicines, and was used on cuts and wounds. It can be recognised by its long-drawn-out flower spike. Ribwort Plantain has long, narrow, ribbed leaves, and a shorter, darker flowerhead, and the Hoary Plantain, most common on chalk and limestone soils, has the largest flowerhead, surrounded by a mist of floating pink and purple anthers.

Several larger plants do not seem to mind the exhaust fumes on busy roads and grow on road verges, their flowers sometimes blackened by mud and smoke from passing cars. The tough Yarrow is one of the most common of roadside plants. It has long, narrow, much-divided leaves with a faint but pleasant smell. The dark styles and white petals together give the flowerheads a greyish look, though sometimes the petals are lilac-coloured, or a darker pinky purple. The Common Mallow also grows well on verges despite the pollution, and will spread into the gutter of a road. It is a handsome plant with strong, rounded leaves and open, pink-petalled, dark-veined flowers.

Near the road or path grow several plants with hooked and clinging fruits that stick to clothing and to the fur of passing animals. For example there are the Burdocks with their large, stiff branches, purple thistle flowers and clinging burs. They grow three feet high: the Common species on dry ground, the Great Burdock with large, rough, downy leaves, on heavier soils. The little yellow flowers of Agrimony grow up tall stems and develop into hooked burs, and one of the few annual Bedstraws, the Goosegrass, distributes little round fruits that feel sticky, but are in fact covered with tiny hooked bristles.

There are several members of the Bedstraw family on roadsides and they are especially common on dry, sunny, well-drained banks. The Heath Bedstraw likes an acid soil, whereas the Lady's Bedstraw, Hedge Bedstraw and Crosswort usually prefer a basic chalk or limestone soil. The generic name, *Galium*, comes from the Greek *gala*, meaning 'milk', for most Bedstraws, have been used for curdling milk. All have weak, clambering stems, with many whorls of leaves. If the plant has a spike of massed, tiny yellow flowers, then it is Lady's Bedstraw, a plant which has a sweet scent when it is dried, and was used as a stuffing for mattresses.

Several species from the Geranium family grow on roadsides. The common Herb Robert, with small, pink, veined flowers and divided, often reddish, leaves can grow from a few inches to over a foot high, among grasses, on walls, or as a garden weed. In southern England, in chalk and limestone country, the large perennial Meadow Cranesbill with its sky-blue, purple-streaked flowers, may grow beside country roads. The Wood Cranesbill of the north is less common, with smaller, darker flowers. The smaller petals of the unusual Dusky Cranesbill are of a subtle

indigo colour with waved edges, the anthers a bright yellow against their dark background.

The Great Mullein is unmistakable and sometimes grows six or seven feet high. It is a biennial. The first year it grows a rosette of thick, pale, furry leaves, and the following year it reaches its full height, with a spike of open yellow flowers that bloom in an irregular fashion, up and down the stalk. There are several other less common species of Mullein including the Dark Mullein, that is found mainly on limy soils in southern England. It differs from the Great Mullein, as it does not have the heavy down on leaf and stalk, but has purple hairs that sprout from the centre of the yellow flowers.

In many parts of the country the roadside is covered in spring by a mass of white umbelliferous flowers. Two that grow in large numbers throughout the British Isles are Cow Parsley and Hogweed, Cow Parsley having the finer, lacy foliage, and Hogweed coarser, broader leaves and larger flowers. The delicate, poisonous Hemlock grows in damp places, and can sometimes be recognised by its purple-spotted stem.

The Wild Carrot and Wild Parsnip are both umbelliferous species. The dense flowerhead of the Wild Carrot or Bird's Nest is white, but the central flower is purple, and is thought to attract pollinating insects. The flat-topped head becomes more and more curved as the seeds mature, until it finally looks like a dry bird's nest. The flowers of the Wild Parsnip are yellow, and as it is the only yellow plant with this form of flower that commonly grows inland, it is easily recognisable.

These are only a few of the many umbelliferous plants that may look confusingly alike at first glance, but can soon be

Wild Carrot *Daucus carota* is a tough coarse plant that grows in grassy places; it is especially common near the sea where it becomes thicker and more luxuriant. The flowers grow in a flat umbel and the central flower is often darker than the rest.

identified when studied more closely.

Another and even more confusing group are the yellow Dandelion-like flowers; these are the Hawkbits, Cat's Ears and Hawkweeds. One way of telling a Cat's Ear from a Hawkbit is to search the flowerheads, for the Cat's Ears have little scales mixed among the florets. However, only the keenest student can tell the difference between the 260 species of Hawkweeds. Other similar species include the little pale-flowered, fine-stalked Nipplewort, the larger and robust Sowthistles, several species of Wild Lettuce and the big, bristly Ox-tongue which grows on limy soils and whose leaves are remarkably like its name.

The most beautiful and graceful of them all is the perennial Goat's Beard. The narrow leaves sheath the stem, which rises to a single yellow flower which is surrounded by a ring of long, narrow, pointed bracts. These fold and enclose the flower by midday, and only open again the next morning, a habit which has given the plant its name of Jack-go-to-bed-at-noon. The round seed head that later develops is similar to that of the Dandelion but larger, lighter, and with fine long plumes.

Some plants now growing mainly on roadsides or on field borders used to be grown as crops by farmers. For instance some Clovers and Vetches, which originally came from abroad, foreign species of Comfrey, and the elegant Sainfoin with its tall pink flower spikes. Madder, Woad and Dyer's Rocket were important dye crops that are now found by the wayside, although they are becoming more rare. The common Wild Teasel with its prickly flowerhead is probably a native plant, but the Fuller's Teasel, now sometimes found on the roadside, was once specially grown and used for raising the 'nap' of cloth.

Of those herbs which used to be grown in gardens, Feverfew is one of the most familiar, with its pretty yellow and white daisy flowers and yellow-green, strong smelling leaves. It still seeds itself on village banks and in the cottage gardens where it was once grown and used as a medicine to reduce fever, a sort of cottage Aspirin. It is never found far from a human dwelling. The leaves of the closely related Tansy are also aromatic. The plant is tall and handsome, and usually grows on damp ground. The yellow button flowers have no petals, and the dark leaves are deeply cut and feathery. The whole plant was used at one time as a medicine to prevent miscarriages, and was also rubbed over meat as a preservative.

Greater Celandine often grows in the long grass in lanes and on field borders close to villages and, despite its name, is a member of the Poppy family. Its rather flimsy yellow flowers have four petals, and when the stem is broken a bright orange, acrid juice oozes out, which was used to cure warts and diseases of the eye.

Finally there is an edible plant, the most delicious of all the Goosefoots, Good King Henry. It grows in rich earth by roads, dung-heaps and farmyards, and its juicy dark leaves are sweeter than spinach.

Sainfoin *Onobrychis viciifolia* is seldom grown as a crop today, but its startlingly pink flower spikes still appear among the grass on roadsides in June, especially on chalk and limestone.

6 Freshwater Flowers

*F*reshwater plant life varies according to the type of soil on the river or pond bed, and the speed of the current. These conditions often change, and many water plants are able to change their shape to suit their situation. Thus some flowering plants such as the Arrowhead or species of the Water Crowfoots can grow in a fast midstream current with long underwater leaves, in slower shallower water with aerial flowering stems and rounder floating leaves, or in muddy shallows with both leaves and stems standing free.

As conditions often prevent water plants from flowering and setting seed, most species are perennial and can reproduce by means of creeping roots or stems, or by the buds that form on leaf edges. The free-floating Duckweeds and Frogbits grow these buds which fall off and sink in the autumn then come up to the surface to grow the following spring. The seeds of water plants are carried off in several ways. Some float until they reach a bank or sink to the mud. Others have burs or hooks which stick to the feet or feathers of waterfowl. Others, such as the White Water Lily or Amphibious Bistort get eaten by ducks or moorhens, then left elsewhere in their droppings.

Although the flora does not suffer from drought it sometimes lacks oxygen, which is plentiful in fast-running streams and rivers but much lacking in slow and still water. Underwater plants, therefore, ensure as much of their surface as possible is exposed to the food in the water. Their leaves are finely divided or in the shape of long, thin straps that move with the current. Those rooted in shallower water and others on the river bank and in marshland have hollow or spongy stems that contain many air spaces and are buoyant.

Many flowering water plants are closely related to those on the land; for instance the Water Crowfoots belong to the same genus as the Buttercups, the Water Violet to the order of the Primulaceae and the Awlwort to the Cruciferae. It is also evident from the form and shape of their flowers and their sexual

OPPOSITE Yellow Water-lily *Nuphar lutea* grows in fresh water where there is little current. The yellow flowers are lifted on stout stalks from among the floating rounded leaves and develop into smooth bulbous fruits; the long roots grow deep into the river mud.

Brooklime *Veronica beccabunga*. Lush and glossy, the Brooklime with its Speedwell flowers creeps and leans beside the water.

Himalayan Balsam *Impatiens glandulifera* was introduced in the nineteenth century and has spread rapidly along the waterways of Britain. The plants flower from July and can grow in large thickets, supplanting the native vegetation. The seeds are hurled from the ripe capsules and quickly germinate.

characteristics that all water plants lived on the land for a long time and only went back to the water fairly recently. Most of these plants still have to blossom above the surface of the water; some, such as the Canadian Pondweed, can flower underwater.

Running water

Northern rivers and streams usually run fast and shallow over rocky beds, and few plants can survive in the water. Mosses and Liverworts grow over the damp boulders, and when the streams fall through the steep northern wooded ravines of ash and yew, the big hollow-stemmed Globe Flower and masses of strong-smelling Ramsons grow alongside.

Several species recently brought to this country grow on the banks and in the shallows of swift-running streams. The wild blue Lupin is only found on the shingle banks of northern rivers, but the yellow Monkey Flower is widespread, growing on the banks of northern burns and among the Cresses in southern chalk streams. There are two species: one has small red spots and comes from North America; the other is from Chile and is less common, the yellow flowers marked with large red blotches. Both were grown in nineteenth-century gardens and spread rapidly by seed. These float, then fill with water and sink to the bottom where they begin to grow. Later they come up again as floating seedlings and finally root in shallow water.

Although the native yellow-flowered Balsam grows in damp places in the north-west of Britain, and two other foreign species are locally common, the recently introduced pink-flowered Himalayan Balsam, or Policeman's Helmet, is the largest and has become the most prolific. It spreads by hurling its seeds violently from the ripe capsules and, although it has a life cycle of one year like all the Balsams, the seedlings grow so fast that thickets of red-stemmed plants, sometimes six or seven feet high, grow everywhere along watersides and sometimes even roadsides. They do not seem to mind polluted places and will grow on canal banks in the bleakest of industrial wastelands.

One of our most familiar water plants, the Watercress, is found in running water and can grow in a very fast current. It thrives in limy areas. Masses of white flowers appear from May to October. They have four petals, like all the members of the Cruciferae family, an order that contains so many edible plants. Both native species, one green-leaved and the other brown-leaved in winter, and also a hybrid that is often found, contain

Arrowhead *Sagittaria sagittifolia*. The distinctive leaves of the Arrowhead are lifted above the water; below the surface are soft, strap-shaped leaves, and round leaves float on the surface. The flowers grow in aerial spikes, each with three white petals, and these are followed by round, knobby fruits. It grows most frequently in the south of England, and is surrounded here by the floating leaves of Duckweed.

Yellow Flag *Iris pseudacorus* is Britain's most common wild Iris, and grows in large clumps in shallow water with fine yellow flowers and long sheathed buds.

quantities of Vitamin C and have been eaten as a salad and as a protection against scurvy for hundreds of years. Brooklime is another plant that grows in large numbers in the shallows of swift-running streams. It is a fleshy stemmed, glossy leaved member of the Speedwell genus, with larger blue flowers than most Speedwells and the charming scientific name of *Veronica beccabunga*.

The broad, wrinkled leaves of the Water Figwort often stay green throughout the winter. It can survive a constant battering from the current because its roots are wedged between stones or cracks in the rock. The tight purple-green flowers are similar to those of the Knotted Figwort that grows in drier places and, like them, are pollinated by wasps. The Western Figwort grows in damp places in the south-west. So does another member of the family. This is the Cornish Moneywort, that creeps over wet rocks and mud by streams and springs with little round hairy leaves and tiny pinkish flowers.

The slow-flowing currents and often rich silt of rivers and streams in southern and Midland counties mean that plants grow thick and well there. They are at their best in high summer, when the shaded woodland flowers are over, and flowers on down and high pasture have withered under the full strength of the sun.

The plant life of rivers or streams can be divided into zones from midstream to bank. Long swaying fronds and strap-shaped leaves grow underwater in the faster midstream current, and closer inshore there are many water plants with submerged and floating leaves and aerial flowers. One of the most familiar of these is the Yellow Water Lily. This plant can survive some movement in the water (unlike the White Water Lily which is generally found only in still water) and has soft underwater leaves as well as the more rigid, floating, oval type. The shining stocky flowers grow up on thick strong stems, and smell faintly of brandy dregs which, together with the shape of the large seed capsules, has given it the country name of Brandy Bottle. The enormous rootstocks can grow nine feet long in the mud of the river bed and the seed heads will eventually release bags of black floating seeds.

The Water Crowfoot will flower in a gentle current, lifting white-petalled, yellow-eyed flowers above the water, and the pink flowers of the Amphibious Bistort, very like the flowers of the Bistort of damp northern meadows, grow from their long, many-jointed, underwater stems. In slower water there may be groups of Water Plantains which have three-petalled, pink or white flowers and broad leaves with a pronounced ribbing, similar to the land Plantains. The flowers of the related Arrowhead are larger and have three petals and purple centres. They grow high up on long stalks and are surrounded by aerial leaves which look like drawn-out arrows.

Towards the river bank there is likely to be a reedswamp group of Bulrushes and Bur-reeds, sometimes joined in the south by the rarer Flowering Rush, with its head of pink three-petalled, three-sepalled flowers, or by the Yellow Flag. This fine Iris can grow six feet tall. The sheathed buds unfold into rich yellow flowers.

The reeds and rushes prevent the current disturbing the mass of plants which grow in the mud on the river edge and up the bank behind. Forget-me-nots, species of the umbelliferous Water Dropwort and the pink and blue flower spikes of Water Speedwells grow rooted underwater, or in drying mud, as the water-level rises and falls. Great clumps of herbaceous perennial plants with sweet smells and bright flowers attract many pollinating insects, bees, flies and beetles, the wasps which visit the Water Figwort and clouds of butterflies to the soft rosy flowerheads of Hemp Agrimony.

The unrelated Purple and Yellow Loosestrifes and the Great Hairy Willowherb with downy stems and leaves and open pink flowers, all grow four or five feet high. The flower spike of the Great Water Dock may grow six feet above its curving pointed leaves. Two members of the Daisy family are common: the Sneezewort, whose greyish-white flowers are like those of the smaller Yarrow, and the yellow-flowered, downy-stemmed Fleabane. This name and the generic name *Pulicaria*, from the Latin word for 'flea', comes the fact that when the plant is burnt its smoke will keep away fleas and other insects. The related Ploughman's Spikenard will have the same effect and is sometimes called Great Fleabane.

Beneath these tall plants grow those that are one or two feet high. There is the large, fleshy Water Chickweed with starry white flowers; Water Avens, that is similar to the Wood Avens but has drooping, orangey-pink flowers, and the Skullcap, whose long blue and white labiate flowers grow in pairs from the axils of paired leaves. The Soapwort sometimes grows on riverbanks, with richly scented, often double, pink blossoms each of which grows from a long pale calyx. Soapwort used to be grown in cottage gardens, as its leaves and roots were used for a washing soap.

The Comfrey also grows in large groups. It can be immediately recognised by its many lanceolate leaves that curve with a pointed tip. The cream and purple, bell-shaped flowers open first at the bottom of the curving stalk and then upwards throughout the summer. The country names of Knitbone and Boneset, the generic name of *Symphytum* (from the Greek *symphyo* – 'to unite'), and the name Comfrey itself, a corruption of *con firma*, all come from its use for stopping bleeding and for setting bones. Many stories were told of its healing powers, which may have had some truth in them as a certain substance called Allantoin, which comes from its roots, is now manufactured artificially and is used in the treatment of wounds, burns and ulcers.

The quick lush growth of the Comfrey leaves led to the introduction of the Prickly Comfrey, a larger, blue-flowered variety from the Caucasus, in 1811. This was supposed to be a wonderful new fodder plant but was a failure, because it was

Purple Loosestrife *Lythrum salicaria* is a big perennial plant with tall purple flower spikes, that grows in clumps on the banks of rivers and streams. Other large river plants such as Great Hairy Willowherb, Yellow Flag and Comfrey often grow alongside.

neither as edible nor as nutritious as it was claimed to be. It now grows wild by roadsides and in damp places, and is sometimes grown for compost.

Still water

Few plants grow around the lakes and tarns of northern Britain for the surrounding rock is often acidic and unyielding, and produces little silt. The flowering plants most likely to grow in the clear stony shallows are the little white-flowered Awlwort, and the taller Water Lobelia, with its spike of spare, lilac flowers.

When the tarn is bordered by a bog, then a peaty, acid silt may be washed into the water, and the yellow flowers of the Lesser Bladderwort and small Yellow Water Lilies may float upon the surface, and the pink and white fringed flowers of the Bogbean grow rooted in the mud. If left alone the plants would lead to a gradual silting up of the tarn, in which more and more bog plants, tussocky Heather hummocks and bog moss would grow, so that eventually the open water would disappear. However, such a progression is often halted by the grazing of sheep and deer.

Most of the natural still water in lowland Britain has been drained and turned into farmland, but there are many man-made reservoirs, gravel-workings, ponds, canals, dikes and ditches. Some artificial waterways were dug a long time ago – the Norfolk Broads, for instance, are the result of extensive peat-digging in medieval times. If left undisturbed, all are subject to the natural plant succession that will eventually completely change them. First decaying matter will steadily collect and raise the bed of pond or ditch. Next reeds, sedges and other water plants will grow out into the open water, each providing a firmer base for those that follow. Then marsh or fen plants will begin to take over, and the final stage in such a process might be a thicket of alder trees or a damp oakwood. Such a process can be stopped by regularly clearing the silt by shovel or dredger, and by reed-cutting, peat-digging, grazing and mowing. Sometimes local factors such as the wash from holiday motor boats and the breeding of escaped Coypu rats in East Anglia have altered the pattern.

The numbers of pondweeds that grow in still water are very different from one year to the next. Sometimes they grow thickly, sometimes there are none at all. The spread of the Canadian Pondweed is a good example.

Bogbean *Menyanthes trifoliata* grows rooted in shallow water and in marshes, fens and bogs.

The dark green leaves of the Canadian Pondweed grow in groups of three along the stem, and the pink flowers bloom underwater, seldom setting fertile seed, for most of the plants in this country are female. Instead, buds form on the stem tips, then in the autumn they fall off and sink with the weight of their food supplies. In the spring when the supplies are used up the lightened buds rise again. They also reproduce by means of their brittle stems which easily break off and quickly develop into new plants. In 1842 the plant was found growing in a Berwickshire lake, and five years later it was noticed in Leicestershire, at the centre of the canal system, along which it speedily spread. Then in 1848 it was found in large numbers near Nottingham, and in 1850 in Warwickshire. A piece of the stem of this Pondweed, put into a stream near Cambridge in 1848 had soon multiplied to choke most of the surrounding watercourses, and it became a pest throughout the country, even blocking the Thames in places. However, having reached its peak, it went into a slow decline, and is now a settled and fairly common inhabitant of canals and ditches. There are several theories put forward to explain this behaviour, one being that the plant is eventually weakened by its method of reproduction; another and more likely argument is that the plant depends on some particular food in the water, and declines as this food disappears.

Free-floating, rootless plants such as the Duckweeds, Bladderworts and Frogbits can only grow in sheltered places, protected from current and wind. The minute leaves and hanging thread-like roots of the Duckweed are quick to grow in still water in a pond, ditch or even cattle-trough. Flowers seldom appear, but on a warm summer's day in shallow water, a mass of tiny white blossoms may cover the surface of the water. The Least Duckweed, a mere green dot, is the smallest of Britain's flowering plants.

The round leaves of the Frogbit are a dark, bronzed green, and the three white petals have yellow markings at their base. Its rarer relative, the Water Soldier, that is found mainly in eastern England, spends part of its life free-floating. It spends the winter underwater, rooted to the pond bed, but each spring the roots loosen their hold and the plant slowly rises as a ring of saw-edged leaves. It then produces large, white, three-petalled blossoms above the surface.

Another water plant that flowers in still water is the Water Violet, whose finely divided leaves are mainly underwater, but whose lilac-petalled, yellow-eyed flowers grow high above the surface. Despite its name, the plant belongs to the Primrose family and, like the Primrose, the flowers are pin-eyed or thrum-eyed to help cross-pollination. The waxen White Water Lily, whose leaves are rounder than those of the Yellow Water Lily, may float further out in deeper water, for its bending stems can grow ten feet long. As the flower petals fall and the seed head ripens it sinks beneath the surface, to release small pink seeds that float slowly away, or are eaten by moorhens.

7 Fen and Marshland Flowers

Greater Bladderwort *Utricularia vulgaris*. The rootless plants of Bladderwort drift submerged in still water, and raise their fine yellow two-lipped flowers above the surface in midsummer. Small bladders on the feathery leaves trap water fleas and other insects and absorb nourishment from them.

A description of the plant life found in still water leads naturally to that of marsh and fenland. Many marsh plants are known to have been common during the Late-glacial period when they provided rich food for the huge, herbivorous elk and bison. Valerian, Meadowsweet and Devil's-bit Scabious were common in this period. The remains of marsh plants such as the Marsh Cinquefoil and Greater Spearwort have been found in even earlier deposits, dating back at least twenty thousand years, to the Full-glacial period.

There is a difference between marsh and fen. Marshland is formed on a slight slope or on low-lying land by a river or stream, where sufficient drainage or regular flooding or scouring stops peat collecting. Fenland, on the other hand, occurs on waterlogged soil near still or slow-moving water, where plant remains are unable to decay normally due to the lack of oxygen in the sodden ground, and peat is formed. Fen peat, unlike the acid bog peat, is alkaline. It forms in areas of basic soils, and is usually made up of the remains of reedswamp plants.

Despite the difference in the make-up of the soil of marsh and fen, the waterlogged, alkaline conditions are similar and both have similar plant life. Sometimes the plants will build up on top of each other until they are no longer affected by the basic water at ground-level. When this happens the soil may become acidic and eventually form a bog peat. This does not happen much in Britain but many of the huge raised bogs in Ireland cover original fenland.

Fens

There are few fens of any size left in Britain, for most have been drained. Some fragments remain round the borders of lakes and river estuaries, but the largest remaining area of fenland is in East Anglia, where the low-lying country is fed by water draining from the surrounding chalk. The development of scrub and woodland has been prevented, partly by man, who has cut reeds, dug peat and farmed the swampy meadows for many hundreds of years, and partly by regular flooding as the sea-level has risen and fallen.

In the open water among the reedswamps float Water Lilies, Water Soldiers, Frogbits and Bladderworts, and some species of Water Plantains. From the shaky platforms of dead reeds grow some tall umbellifers – the rare Milk Parsley that provides food for the caterpillars of the Swallowtail butterfly, and the common

PREVIOUS PAGES Marsh Marigold or Kingcup *Caltha palustris* flowers early in marshy places from March to June and is common from the south of England north to Iceland. The shining yellow flowers resemble those of a larger Buttercup and the leaves are rounded and darkly glossy.

Wild Angelica *Angelica sylvestris* grows in damp shady places, on the borders of low-lying woods and in fens and marshes. The plants are tall, hollow stemmed, with smooth graceful leaves divided into leaflets, and the umbels of flowers are white, or occasionally rosy-tinted. The inflated sheaths enclose the leaf stalks and these help to distinguish the Angelica from other similar umbellifers.

Wild Angelica. Cowbane and Water Parsnip, which sometimes grow six feet high, and the shorter Water Dropwort also grow there. The rare purple Marsh Pea and White Climbing Fumitory twist up the reed stems, and the Great Spearwort, a tall buttercup with long pointed leaves, grows among them. The tallest of them all, the giant of the fens, is the Marsh Sowthistle, a ten-foot perennial with lemon-yellow flowers. Among the rarest is the Fen Orchid, a small plant with yellow-green flowers and a pair of broad leaves.

A neglected fen may become colonised by bog plants or, most commonly, by numbers of woody plants such as Bog Myrtle and Red and Blackcurrant bushes, followed by bushes of Sallow, Guelder Rose, Privet and Buckthorn. Many herbaceous plants will then die through lack of light, and will leave ferns, Stinging Nettles and Brambles to grow in an often impenetrable tangle on the swampy ground beneath leaning alder and buckthorn. These unstable trees will finally fall, and will provide a more solid base for permanent alder wood or oakwood.

Holiday water traffic has been mentioned as a recent influence on fen plants, and this is particularly apparent on the Norfolk Broads, where the reedswamps are often stopped from growing too far out into the water by the continuous backwash from boats. The reeds have also been eaten in quantities by Coypus, thus creating wide areas of mud-flats. The first Coypus escaped from a local fur farm in 1937 and, as these large rodents breed very quickly and eat a lot of water plants, they soon changed the character of the plant life in parts of the fens. Some of their favourite plants became increasingly rare, such as the Great Water Dock, Hemp Agrimony, Great Hairy Willow-herb and Cowbane (the latter being a surprising choice, as it is extremely poisonous to cows and humans). At the same time Purple Loosestrife, Nettles and Forget-me-nots grew well, because

Hemp Agrimony *Eupatorium cannabinum* is a tall branched plant with flat-topped clusters of flowers ranging in colour from pale pink to reddish mauve. It flowers in July–September in damp woods, marshes or wasteground.

Coypus do not eat them. The harsh winter of 1963 and concentrated trapping have now cut down the numbers of Coypus, and the balance of the flora has been partially restored.

Marshland

Marshland is less easy to define than a peaty fen, for the word is used to describe any waterlogged and permanently muddy area where there is no peat. It can be anything from a lake-shore or flood plain, to the borders of a stream, pond or ditch. Typical marsh plants grow tall and lush, and include many of the river-bank plants described in the earlier chapter.

Among the larger plants grow the Marsh Ragwort, Water and Peppermints, the closely related, white-flowered Gipsy-wort and the medicinal Valerian, which grows to a height of three or four feet and produces clusters of pale pink flowers. The small underground tubers have been used for thousands of years as a soothing and narcotic drug. The Common Meadow Rue grows to a similar height, its pale flowers dominated by masses of long yellow stamens. Marsh and Fen Bedstraws grow at a lower level with long stems and circles of white flowers, which clamber and lean like all the Bedstraw family. The Marsh Cinquefoil, which is most common in the north, bears purple flowers surrounded by larger purple sepals and toothed leaves backed by a pale grey down.

In trodden places and in bare mud grow small creeping plants with rooting stems such as the Silverweed, the little Water Blinks, Mudwort and round-leaved Marsh Pennywort. The tough hot-tasting Water Pepper, relative of the Persicaria and known as 'Arsemart' until Victorian times, also grows here.

The Butterbur is a tough perennial plant which, once it has taken hold, will dominate all other plants in a low-lying meadow or streamside. It is closely related to the Coltsfoot and spreads by similar creeping rootstocks, flowering in February or March, before the appearance of the leaves. The pale pink, tufted clusters of flowers are usually dioecious, that is the male and female flowers are on separate plants, the male flowers growing in shorter spikes and with more nectar than the longer, looser female flowers. The male plants are far more widely distributed than the female, which are mainly found in north-west Britain. This is perhaps because the plants are behaving as separate species each liking a different climate and soil, or it may be that the male plants have been planted further south to provide early

ABOVE Grass of Parnassus *Parnassia palustris* grows chiefly in the north and west on marshy ground. The white flowers appear in June–September. Yellow Bladderwort is blossoming in the background.

BELOW Marsh Helleborine *Epipactis palustris* can grow three feet high on moist, limy soil. It is uncommon but is found in all parts of England, Wales and southern Scotland.

BELOW Amphibious Bistort *Polygonum amphibium* is a versatile species that can grow in fairly deep water where it has long, rounded, floating leaves, and also on marshy ground, when the leaves are shorter and downy. The pink flowers are lifted above the water towards the end of summer, and are similar to those of the closely related Persicaria and Bistort.

nectar for bees. The great leaves appear in April as the flowers die, and are often three feet across, with pale downy undersides.

One of the most beautiful of marsh plants, usually found in the north and west of Britain, is the Grass of Parnassus, whose white, five-petalled flowers might be mistaken at first glance for those of the Meadow Saxifrage. However, the flowers grow singly from the graceful stem, unlike the clustered flowers of the Saxifrage. The petals are finely veined with green, and at the end of each of the hairs that surrounds the stamens hangs a shining yellow gland. The Marsh Helleborine is a more obviously striking plant, with pink and white yellow-throated flowers that are larger than those of most Helleborine species. It grows in open ground whereas other Helleborines prefer shade. Both the Marsh Helleborine and the Grass of Parnassus grow well in those marshy areas between sand-dunes known as 'dune slacks'. These are oases of fresh water in which a surprising variety of marsh plants will grow.

The Buttercup family is found in many wet places, as implied by the name of the large genus *Ranunculus*, which comes from the Latin word for 'frog' – *rana*. The Water Crowfoots belong to this genus, but these plants do not seem to have the acrid quality of the land Buttercups. The Greater and Lesser Spearworts of the fens and the Celery-leaved Buttercup of marshy ground poison cattle and sheep when eaten fresh. The latter, which bears very small yellow flowers and long fruits is also known as 'Blisterwort'. The Meadow and Creeping Buttercups are most common on damp ground, but flower later than the magnificent Marsh Marigold or Kingcup, whose glossy yellow blossoms, made up of shining sepals, and dark polished foliage, appear in March and April. With spreading roots and creeping stems the plant will grow in large numbers in marshy meadows as far north as Iceland, and may have lived through the ice ages in this country.

Several species from the genus *Polygonum* grow in water-meadows. All have the same compact heads of small pink, red or white flowers and long jointed stems. The most common are the Persicaria or Redleg and the Pale Persicaria, which are also found as weeds in fields and gardens, and the Amphibious Bistort which will sometimes grow on land, when its leaves will become more rounded and hairy. The largest of the Polygonum species is the Bistort, which is seldom found in the south, but is fairly common in wet northern fields where it has also been grown as a vegetable and is used in making the Cumberland herb pudding. The strange name of Bistort refers to the twisted rootstock and comes from the Latin *bis* and *torta*, meaning 'twice-twisted'.

Marshy meadows suit the several species of Marsh Orchid, which vary in colour from yellow to magenta-purple. Among the lush grasses, rushes and sedges grow the Devil's Bit Scabious, the tall, pale Marsh Woundwort and the Nodding Bur-marigold. Many of these species grow in water meadows with the Meadow-sweet, Ragged Robin and Milkmaid, and a section on this type of land and its plants in included in the chapter on Grasslands.

8 Heath, Moor and Bogland Flowers

*T*he majority of the grassy lowland heaths of the south and east, and the high heather moors of the north and west, were originally covered by forests, but were cleared long ago to provide rough grazing land. The poverty of the soil has often prevented trees from growing again, and farmers grazing sheep and cattle and burning the heather have kept the land clear of young saplings. Peat-bog, on the other hand, has developed naturally and is now being slowly destroyed by man, who has cut peat fuel for centuries and who has drained many bogs to provide further grazing land.

There is not such a wide variety of plants growing on these acid soils as there is on chalk and limestone. They are mostly Heather plants or bog mosses, with few undershrubs and herbs.

Heathland

The lowland heaths of Surrey, Hampshire and East Anglia have developed on poor sandy soils. Where the land has been heavily grazed, little annual plants and mosses will grow over the open ground.

Parsley Piert – a tiny Lady's Mantle – and Least Bird's Foot grow over the closely bitten turf on anthills, and among the longer tougher grasses plants such as Tormentil and Heath Bedstraw, which like an acid soil, will grow. Bracken will sometimes dominate for it spreads onto grassland with creeping underground stems and drifting seed spores, and is not eaten by animals.

Gorse bushes are common everywhere on sandy southern commons, and in July and August the dry seed pods can be heard popping loudly as they burst open. The glossy seeds are flung to the ground some distance from the bush, and as they have an oily attachment which attracts ants, they are sometimes dragged off and left along the bare earth of the ants' run. Like the Broom, the Gorse seedling bears small leaves, but these soon drop, and the sharp narrow stems serve the same purpose as leaves.

The Broom is a close relation, which grows in dry, stony places. It is perhaps as a symbol of persistance that the sprig of Broom has been adopted as a heraldic device in France and England. Our Plantagenet kings took their name from the medieval word for Broom – the *Planta genista*. It is interesting to notice the number of heath plants that have narrow, hard leaves or stems, whose shiny

PREVIOUS PAGES Harebell *Campanula rotundifolia* begins to flower in July, and the delicate blue bells hanging from their fine stem grow everywhere in Britain on dry, grassy heaths and downs.

OPPOSITE Gorse *Ulex europaeus*. The richly scented flowers are at their best in early summer; later in the year the ripe pods explode with loud pops to throw out the seeds. Spiny green stems do the work of leaves, and as they lose little moisture they are well adapted to dry and droughty conditions.

surfaces form a protection from the drying winds.

If the Foxglove is found it usually means that the soil is acid. It grows on heaths and banks and in open woodland. It is a biennial, which grows a rosette of large, slightly downy leaves during its first year and then sends up its tall, familiar, flowering-stem the following year. The hanging pink flowers open at the bottom of the stem first. They have spotted interiors and fine pale hairs which attract the pollinating bees, and each plant has as many as two million seeds.

It is well known that the Foxglove, *Digitalis purpurea*, will slow down and strengthen the heart beat and it is included in the British Pharmacopoeia today. The whole plant is poisonous and its old medicinal use as a purgative and expectorant must have been extremely dangerous.

The wide, sandy heaths of Breckland in East Anglia have been famous for their plant life since John Ray visited them in the seventeenth century. The flowers here are typical of those found on uncultivated, dry, acid soil in south and south-eastern England, but there are also many rarities on the occasional patches of limy soil, where the topsoil has worn away to the chalk rock underneath. Wild Thyme and Harebells, which like any soil that is open and dry, grow among the rough grasses. The creeping Mossy Tillaea forms red mats over closely grazed turf, and the Breckland or Spanish Catchfly grows two feet tall, with little greenish-yellow flowers all round the sticky, fly-trapping stem. Four rare species of Speedwell grow here, and also the fine-stemmed Breckland Wormwood.

The scrub and Heather which used to be kept down by the grazing of stock and rabbits is now spreading.

Bird's Foot Trefoil *Lotus corniculatus* flowers abundantly in dry grassland everywhere throughout the summer. The red buds open into bright peaflowers; the ripe pods blacken and curl into the shape of a bird's claw.

The pale purple flowers of Heather *Calluna vulgaris*, which is in bloom from July to September, form a carpeting undershrub covering vast areas of the countryside.

Heather, or Ling, is the most common plant on poor, lightly grazed soil, and is widespread and familiar on heath and moorland. It survives on this poor soil with the help of a particular fungus that invades the roots and tissues of the plant and helps provide its food. The tough-stemmed clumps live for about twenty-five years, growing tall and leggy if left undisturbed, and short and compact when grazed. They will cover very large areas, sometimes mixed with tough grasses and sedges. Heather often grows with bright purple Bell Heather plants and Fine-leaved Heath in dry areas, and with Cross-leaved Heath on damper ground. Dorset Heath is a tall, downy species with long flower spikes, that only grows in the West Country, and it is unusual to find Cornish Heath anywhere but on the Lizard Peninsula. But it is in the north and west that the vast tracts of moorland occur.

Moorland

The moorlands on hard, acidic rock are often modified and controlled by grazing, burning and draining. Natural moorland is mainly found above the tree-line on well-drained mountain slopes.

Regular burning of moorland is one of the oldest and easiest methods of destroying invading scrub and saplings, to clear the moor for sheep and grouse. The woody Heather roots can survive the burning and produce new shoots, and the many Heather seeds soon grow again, to provide fresh and tasty grazing; but the delicate herbs that will grow among the Heather plants are often killed.

When Heather plants are left undisturbed for some length of time, and become long and lanky, there is space and light enough for some heath plants to grow. The Heath Spotted Orchid grows better on an acid soil, unlike the majority of the species, and is to be found on southern heaths and on high moorland, from Wales to the Orkneys and as far north as Iceland. Its leaves are lightly spotted, and the short, pale flower spikes are delicately patterned with a darker pink. The Lesser Butterfly Orchid will also grow in acid soils, and bears widely spaced, long-spurred creamy flowers that are visited by butterflies and moths.

Two semi-parasitic members of the Figwort family will grow among the Heather. One is the Lousewort which is a creeping perennial, similar to the Red and Yellow Rattles, with bright

Bilberry *Vaccinium myrtillus*. The pinkish bell flowers of this little shrub are replaced by an edible black berry with a purple bloom in late summer. On high moors and open woodland the Bilberry may be a dominant plant, but on lower ground it is most likely to grow beneath Heather clumps.

pink flowers growing out of its inflated calyx. The other, the Common Cow-wheat, has thin stems, long paired leaves, and pale pink or yellow flowers.

The only other shrub that grows in any quantity on the moor is Bilberry. It prefers a shadier and drier position than Heather, and will grow low beneath Heather clumps, or will grow on its own along woodland borders. The rare Dwarf Cornel grows among it in the Scottish Highlands, a plant that is surprisingly related to the Dogwood, the red-branched shrub that grows ten feet high on southern chalk and limestone. The little eight-inch Dwarf Cornel has smaller leaves of a similar shape, that grow in pairs from the stem.

There are two types of moorland, 'thin' and 'fat', although similar plants are found on both. Thin moorland is formed on shallow, acid, well-washed soil, on which trees may once have grown. Fat moorland develops on deep, raw, peaty soil that was originally bog, but which has been drained. This type of moorland is often damp; Cross-leaved Heath begins to take over from the Heather, and bog plants and mosses grow there.

Bogland

Three types of bog can be recognised in this country, though each tends to grade into the other, and there is no clear division between them.

Valley bog is formed in any undrained dip or heathland valley that becomes saturated with acid water. Southern bogs are usually of this type, and those in the New Forest are especially well known for their flowers. Raised or domed bogs are now found mainly in Ireland, though some still exist in northern Britain, in areas of high rainfall. In this case the peat builds up over fen plants or valley bog, sometimes to a depth of fifteen feet or more, and will continue to develop so long as the climate is damp enough. Blanket bog forms along the western half of Britain, from Dartmoor to Sutherland, wherever there is un-drained, acid soil, high rainfall, and moist winds. The plants vary from Heather in the drier parts to Sphagnum moss and other bog mosses, and sedges which are found round the dark, peaty pools.

There is a general lack of nitrogen in peat, for the bacteria that normally decay organic matter and produce nitrogen are unable to survive in the airless atmosphere, so many bog plants have had to obtain nitrates from other sources. The Heather, as described above, gets its food from a certain type of fungus. Bog Myrtle, a sweetly scented little shrub with short, reddish catkin flowers, has nodules containing nitrogen attached to its roots, the Sundews and Butterworts have leaves that catch and then digest small insects, while the Bladderwort plants can trap small water insects.

There are three species of Sundew, so named after the sticky 'dew' drops that hang from the red hairs on each leaf. Insects, attracted to the glistening drops, are caught and bent slowly towards the centre of the leaf, where they are digested. The Great Sundew has leaves four inches long; the most common species has short, round leaves, the third has oblong leaves, and all have a little head of white flowers on a long stalk at the centre of the plant.

The broad leaves of the Butterwort look oily and are a pale yellow-green, with curled edges. They wait like sticky tongues for insects to land, then roll inwards, enclosing their prey. The Common Butterwort has a beautiful, delicate, purple flower with a long spur, a white throat, and a spreading lobed lip. These species will not grow in the most saturated and acid ground, but prefer damp heaths and even limy fen and marshland. The leaves can be used to curdle fresh milk, and are also bruised and applied to the chapped udders of cows.

The related Bladderwort floats, half-submerged and rootless, in peaty pools and other still water. It lifts its spurred yellow flowers, of a similar form to those of the Butterwort, above the surface, and is surrounded by finely divided leaves. Water fleas and other insects are trapped and digested in the many little bladders that grow among the leaves.

The Cranberry and Bog Rosemary are two other members of the Heather family that grow in tussocks across the bogs, and a member of the Lily family is common – the Bog Asphodel. This lovely plant, with its spike of yellow flowers and waving red anthers, has been used as a dye for both hair and cloth.

Long-leaved Sundew *Drosera intermedia*. An uncommon Sundew found in bogs and damp heathland. The leaves, with their sticky glistening red hairs, curve inwards to digest trapped insects. The Common Sundew has rounder leaves, and all species flower in midsummer when a long stalk grows from the rosette of leaves, topped by a small head of white flowers.

9 Mountain Flowers

*T*he greatest variety of British mountain plants survive in small, scattered groups in the north and north-west. They are the survivors of species that grew throughout Britain on the borders of glaciers during the ice ages and were well adapted to the cold weather that lasted for centuries as the ice melted.

As thick vegetation and forests covered the land these Alpine and Arctic plants were smothered, and could only survive on open mountain-tops and some sea cliffs.

The rich soils that suit many mountain plants have been steadily washed away by rain, and peat-bogs and acid moorland have developed over much of the high ground. They now grow on exposed ridges and outcrops of calcareous rock, half-stabilised screes, cliffs and gullies. These habitats can be small and specialised; on the lee-side of a boulder, for example, a group of plants may be protected from the wind and the freezing winter temperatures, and snow will cover them.

Saxifrages and Stonecrops may grow from a sheltered spot on a cliff face, their long roots tucked deeply into a rocky crevice. Water percolating from among the rocks may carry rich mineral salts, leached from above, and such places will be marked by bright green mosses and liverworts and sometimes a group of flowering plants.

The mountains that are composed of basic, alkaline rocks are those which support the greatest variety of plants. The hard volcanic rock in the Lake District and Snowdonia is basic but weathers slowly, retaining its sharp peaks and crags and possessing a fairly limited flora. The surrounding smoother mountains, however, are made up of softer, acidic slates and shales. The Cairngorms in the eastern Scottish Highlands are mainly composed of hard acidic granite which weathers to a coarse gravel. The rarest and most numerous mountain species are found on patches of carboniferous limestone in northern England and north-west Scotland, on the soft, easily weathered mica-schist of the central Scottish Highlands, and on the basic volcanic rock of parts of the western Highlands and Islands.

Mountain plants have to tolerate severe conditions. The rain, snow and frost constantly attack the rock, causing it to crack; the ground is unstable and exposed to high winds, high rainfall and high humidity. The soil is generally poor, and the low temperatures mean that the growing season only lasts three to four months. In addition to all this the land is often grazed on by sheep and deer.

The difficulties faced by the flora have also hindered botanists, and there is still much to be learnt about the distribution and habits of mountain plants. Three new species have been discovered during the past thirty-five years, all growing in remote, bare and stony places. The *Koenigia islandica* with its fat stem and rounded succulent leaves, which seldom creeps more than an inch or two across the stones, is an Arctic plant, as is the *Diapensia lapponica* which grows in tight shining cushions dotted with creamy flowers. The third, the Scottish variety of *Artemisia*

PREVIOUS PAGES Alpine Cinquefoil *Potentilla crantzii* grows in a few scattered places in the north; this photograph was taken on Ben Lawers, a Scottish mountain that is botanically famous. The large flowers are often spotted with orange, and bloom in June and July.

norvegica, is a little downy plant with a hairy stem and drooping flower.

Mountain species, that is those which can grow above two thousand feet, have similar ways of dealing with these bad conditions. The most obvious of these is the way they grow close to the ground forming dense cushions, mats and rosettes, such as Moss Campion, Alpine Cinquefoil, Lady's Mantle and the Saxifrages; or creeping, dwarfed woody plants such as the Mountain Avens and mountain Willows. Such forms give protection from wind and weather, and little time and energy is used to produce flower and fruit from the short stems during the brief summer. The bright light at high altitudes also affects the shapes of these plants, for such light limits their growth, just as a dark cupboard encourages a bulb stem to grow tall. The pigment in flower petals is also affected by the intensity of the light so that many mountain plants possess brilliantly coloured flowers.

Mountain plants have to be perennial, and as their seed cannot always ripen during a cold summer they must be able to re-produce in other ways, usually by creeping rhizomes or underground rooting stems. The rare Drooping Saxifrage seldom flowers and has never been known to fruit, even in its Arctic habitats. Instead it reproduces by means of bright red axillary bulbils that fall from the plant in the autumn. The Alpine Bistort has similar bulbils growing among its pink flowers. Two exceptions to the perennial rule are the brilliant blue annual Snow

Gentian that only flowers in direct sunlight, and the *Koenigia islandica*, or Iceland Purslane.

Most of the flowering herbaceous plants spend the winter just above or below the surface of the soil. Many have leaves and stems covered with protective hairs, roots filled with a store of food, and buds often fully formed in the autumn, ready to spring up at the first signs of a thaw. Only one strictly mountain species winters as a bulb, for the deeper soil levels are likely to remain frozen well into the summer months, which slows the growth of bulbous or deep-rooted plants. This is the delicate Snowdon Lily, whose single white flowers are veined with purple. Its only British habitat is Snowdonia which is surprising, since it grows on the Alps, the Himalayas, and in the mountains of Asia and America.

The bright colours and the structure of many mountain flowers might suggest that they are pollinated by insects, but in fact this is seldom the case. Self-pollination is the most usual method, probably because there are very few insects in such a harsh climate. The Alpine Catchfly, for example, is pollinated by butterflies in the Alps, but has to rely on self-pollination in the Scottish Highlands. Another group of plants seem to have normal flowers and seeds, but the pollen does not ripen and the seeds ripen without being fertilised. Such plants are called 'apomictic' and include the Alpine Lady's Mantles and mountain Hawkweeds as well as many common lowland species.

Apart from some sub-species of Hawkweeds and small-flowered northern Eyebrights, no mountain plants have been found that only grow in Britain. Some of our rarities also grow in the Arctic, some brightly-flowered species grow among the Alps, but most are found both in the Arctic and on Alpine mountains.

Among the mountain species are many plants which also grow in the lowlands, but these are often shorter and have larger flowers and seeds than those at lower altitudes. Buttercups, Speedwells and Mouse-ear Chickweeds are among those that vary in this way.

The vegetation covering a mountain composed of acidic rock will be mainly of moorland species, and on a basic rock there will be grassland species. Above the tree-line on granite or other acidic rock there will almost certainly be a broad zone of Heather, with perhaps an undershrub layer of Bearberry, a trailing evergreen with pale pink flowers and bright red berries. Higher up the Heather plants become scarce, usually being replaced above three thousand feet by rough dense shrubs of Bilberry, with their juicy, dark, mauve-bloomed fruit, and creeping Crowberry plants. The tiny pink flowers of the Crowberry bloom early in the year, and the large berries change from green to pink to purple, and finally to black. The Bilberry and a lowland species of Crowberry can also grow on lower moorland, but there they are not so common as Heather. Another high-altitude shrub, the Cloudberry, only grows in peat-bogs and produces small fruits that look like yellow blackberries.

The flowering plants likely to be found growing on higher

ABOVE Purple Saxifrage *Saxifraga oppositifolia* is often planted in garden rockeries but its true habitat is high in the Scottish mountains, and occasionally in limestone areas in Yorkshire. The bright short-stalked flowers growing from a close mat of creeping stems and hairy leaves are typical of many mountain plants.

RIGHT Starry Saxifrage *Saxifraga stellaris* is the most common of the mountain Saxifrages, and is able to grow on acid soils. It is most likely to be found in damp places in hilly and mountainous districts in the north, and flowers at midsummer.

acidic rock are few, and may include the Mountain Azalea, the white-flowered Dwarf Cornel, the rare Alpine Sow-Thistle and several Saxifrages. The Starry Saxifrage is one of the most common herbaceous plants on poor mountain soil. It has a little rosette of leaves which root among coarse gravel and stones, and short, reddish, hairy stems carrying white star-flowers, each petal spotted with yellow at the base.

Exposed mountain summits and ridges are often bare of plants. The soil is washed away by heavy rain and the rock cracked by frost. Lichens and colonies of sedges or rushes can sometimes live in sheltered places. Snow may lie in hollows for most of the year and on the borders of a snow patch two flowering plants may grow among the mosses, both protected by a downy covering on leaves or stems. The Dwarf Cudweed is a member of the Daisy family, and grows about two inches high with small brownish flowers; the Alpine Lady's Mantle is also a common plant in the lower mountain pastures and possesses numerous sub-species. It is a charming little plant with a loose head of yellow-green flowers and about five separated leaflets that flash silver in the wind when their downy undersides are exposed.

Such is the plant life to be found on the sides of a granite mountain. The species on a mountain composed of basic rock may be different. Among the scattered rocks below the summit grow mountain species of Pearlwort, Rock Cress and Rock Whitlow Grass, tough little rosette plants whose relatives grow on stone walls, wasteground and sea cliffs in the south. A little lower the large blue flowers of rare Alpine Forget-me-not and Alpine and Rock Speedwells shelter between boulders, among cushions of bright pink-flowered Moss Campion, Thrift, and creamy-flowered Mossy Cyphel.

Water which oozes or trickles from among the stones, enriched by salts from the rock, is known as 'flush' water, and such flushes may vary in size from a damp patch that feeds a hump of moss and a rosette of Golden Saxifrage, to a spring that is swollen each year with melting snow and has, by comparison, fairly lush plants all round it. This is the place to find the sparse little pink-flowered Alpine Willow Herb, the dwarfed mountain Kingcup, Alpine Meadow Rue, Alpine Scurvy Grass, Mountain Sorrel, Alpine Saw-wort with broader downier leaves than the lowland species, and several Saxifrages. One of the most beautiful of these is the Purple Saxifrage, *Saxifraga oppositifolia*, whose large flowers grow from among small dark leaves on prostrate stems.

Sometimes the vegetation round such a flush on a damp rock ledge, which is safe from grazing animals, will spread outwards on a platform of woody mountain willows, providing support for larger plants such as the Globe Flower and Angelica. Then the upper layers of humus may grow above the base-rich water, and heath and bog plants may appear. Often this structure will become top-heavy and, swayed by the wind and weather, will collapse, leaving the whole process to begin again.

The lower flushes that occur on more open ground are often

Roseroot *Sedum rosea*. A thick, succulent plant that is found on mountain ledges and in high rocky crevices in Wales, northern England and Scotland, and occasionally on northern sea cliffs. The dense heads of yellowish flowers with tufted stamens appear in early summer; when cut, the stalks give out a rich rose-like scent.

richer than those above, since more minerals have been able to collect there and they are sometimes further enriched by the dung of animals and birds. Marsh plants such as Butterwort, Water Avens, Meadow Sweet and Alpine Bistort grow among rushes and sedges, but more animals graze at this level and, therefore, there are likely to be fewer herbaceous plants.

Sometimes, in humid, shaded gullies and crevices above two thousand feet, typical woodland plants will grow. Among the mountain Saxifrages, succulent Roseroot with its sweet-scented rootstock, and Alpine Lady's Mantles, there may sometimes be groups of Primroses, Wood Anemones, Wood Sorrel and mauve-flowered Wood Cranesbill. These may be all that is left of a former birch or pinewood, after man has cleared the trees. Straggling, natural birchwood can still be seen growing above two thousand feet on the Cairngorms, mixed with juniper scrub and Heather.

Two mountain plants are especially associated with loose screes and unstable slopes, and both were common throughout the country following the last Ice Age. One is the Shrubby Cinquefoil which seems to have migrated north from the Continent, and is now found on limestone outcrops in the Lake District, Upper Teesdale and shingle banks in Ireland. It is a little bush with greyish pointed leaves and familiar yellow Cinquefoil flowers. The other is the Mountain Avens, *Dryas octopetala*, which is an Arctic/Alpine plant and forms a creeping mat across the stones with woody stems and small, darkly glossy, scalloped leaves with downy silver undersides. The flowers grow singly from the short stems. They usually have eight white petals and a mass of golden stamens. Apart from its beauty, the plant is also important to those tracing the history of the British flora, for it is a typical plant of the Arctic tundra and its presence or absence in the various levels of clay and peat are a sign of the weather at different periods. Both the Mountain Avens and the Crowberry are common plants on the Arctic tundra today, the former on limy soil, the latter on acid and peaty soils.

The flowering plants considered so far have been those growing in rocky places. On the more stable mountain summits there is often a poor grassland which is heavily grazed and unlikely to have many plants growing in it. Even on the soft, rich, mica-schist mountains in the central Highlands it is unusual to find many flowering species on the gently sloping high grasslands. Those who are searching for mountain flowers should climb, in early summer, to steep well-drained slopes where there is too much frost for close grass to grow, yet enough soil for hundreds of small brightly flowering plants among the grasses.

One of the Scottish mountains most famous for its plants is Ben Lawers in central Perthshire, and here on a steep, ungrazed ridge above two thousand feet the pink-, purple- and white-flowered cushions of Saxifrage, Thrift and Sea and Moss Campion, the eight-petalled Mountain Avens and four-petalled Dwarf Cornel grow among the mossy boulders. Between the thin tufts of grass grow Boreal Fleabane, the flowers like mauve daisies on long hairy stems, bright brief-flowering and rare Purple Mountain Milk Vetch, Alpine Lady's Mantle, some of the many varieties of yellow mountain Hawkweeds, the Least Cinquefoil with greyish foliage and tiny yellow flowers and perhaps the rarer Alpine Cinquefoil with large yellow, orange-spotted flowers. There may be mountain species of Eyebright, Mountain Pansy, Speedwell and Forget-me-not, and species that are also found on lowland heaths such as Heath Bedstraw, Tormentil, Harebell, Thyme and Ox-eye Daisy.

One last place to find mountain plants should be mentioned. This is on the north and north-west coasts of Scotland, where high-altitude flora such as the Purple Saxifrage and Mountain Avens grow right down the rocky sea cliffs among the coastal plants, and the Purple Mountain Milk Vetch will sometimes blossom on banks of sand and shingle.

Mountain Avens *Dryas octopetala* is a creeping undershrub that grows in a dense mat across the rocks on limestone mountains in Snowdonia and in the north. The little evergreen leaves are downy on the underside, a habit shared by several other mountain plants; the large white eight-petalled flowers have a boss of golden stamens.

10 Flowers of the Sea Coast

*T*he long British coastline is remarkably varied; there are cliffs of basalt, granite and old red sandstone, chalk and limestone, and low cliffs of soft clay. Ranges of sand-dunes and shingle banks form along the shore, and flat wastes of half-submerged salt-marsh spread alongside the estuaries of rivers. Because of the violent winds and constant salt spray, the shifting of sand and pebbles and the steady wearing away of rock, the land cannot be farmed and much has remained in its natural state.

Trees and scrub will not grow in such conditions and the communities of coastal plants are those that prefer open ground, as they have been for thousands of years. There are many common weeds growing among maritime plants, and it is likely that weeds, such as members of the Cabbage, Dock and Goose-foot families, survived in the open communities along the coast when those growing inland were shaded out by the forests.

Drought is the greatest problem for coastal plants. Even those plants that are submerged by the tide in a salt-marsh can suffer from drought in the summer, when the sea water may contain too much salt.

The water that is absorbed can be quickly lost by evaporation from the surface of the leaves when a plant is exposed to constant

BELOW Sea Pea *Lathyrus japonicus* grows on shingle beaches in southern and eastern England but is an uncommon plant. The leathery leaves and deep roots are typical of many sea-shore plants.

winds, and the most common feature of maritime plants is their tough, shiny leaves. The leathery surface will also protect them from being scratched by blowing sand. The stalks and leaves of species such as the Sea Wormwood and Marsh Mallow are covered by dense, downy hairs to conserve moisture, and many other plants grow in a low, thick cushion to stop water loss.

There are two groups of strictly maritime plants. Those that can survive regular immersion in salt water and drenching salt spray are known as 'halophytes', from the Greek word for 'salt plants'. Most halophytes are perennial and all have thick fleshy leaves, which help them to absorb salt water. The other group have developed long roots to reach water and keep them steady in shifting sand or shingle. Their leaves, too, are succulent, with swollen cells for water storage. They can live in very dry conditions and are called 'xerophytes', from the Greek for 'dry plants'.

Beaches

Apart from Eel-grass, a rudimentary flowering plant that sometimes grows underwater in the shallows, the first sign of vegetation is likely to be at the drift-line. On a sandy beach this may be sparse. For example there could be some casual annual weeds growing among the rubbish, and a species of maritime Knotgrass, or clumps of prickly Saltwort, an annual with sharp-tipped, juicy little leaves and green flowers.

A shingle beach may have a richer soil, made up of rotting rubbish and decaying organic matter, washed up by the tide and lodged among the stones, and in this a surprising number of plants can grow. Conditions are not so severe as they seem, for fresh water is often close beneath the stones, even during a hot summer. It rides above the deeper salt water and is made up of rainwater, dew and moisture condensed on the pebbles.

Many drift-line plants are annuals, quick to grow and take advantage of good conditions in a changing environment. The Sea Rocket is common, a member of the Cabbage family with lilac-pink flowers and succulent leaves, which often becomes large and sprawling by the end of the season. Several members of the Goosefoot family are common on the shingle; there are three maritime species of Orache which look similar to those so common inland, and also the Sea Beet, a perennial with tough shiny leaves and a spike of green flowers. This is the ancestor of our garden beets, and the leaves are delicious eaten

Yellow horned Poppy *Glaucium flavum* has tough, grey-bloomed leaves to withstand sea spray and blowing sand, and deep roots to reach water through the shingle. Conspicuous curving seed pods follow the yellow Poppy flowers. It grows right round the British coastline.

Marram Grass *Ammophila arenaria* colonising a young sand dune. Marram grows abundantly round the coast and is often planted on eroding beaches, for it binds and stabilises the sand with its creeping roots and sharp tough leaves.

Sea Holly *Eryngium maritimum* is becoming less common but is still widespread along the coastline, especially among sand dunes. The roots are deep, to reach fresh water through the sand, the leaves tough, sharp and grey-blue, and the spiny flower head is blue or purple.

when young and tender. Another edible plant that was formerly common on shingle is the Sea Kale, a large perennial crucifer. The leaves are thick and waxy, and the stalks used to be blanched by heaping shingle round the plant.

The shifting sand and gravel actually helps some species to grow. Sea Campion, Sea Sandwort, and the less common Shrubby Sea-blite can not only survive when covered with blown stones or sand, but are then stimulated to send up new shoots, down new roots and to spread in wide mats over sand and shingle. They are more likely to be found higher up the beach beyond the tide-line and, together with other creeping plants such as the Sea Bindweed, Sea Milkwort and yellow-flowered Stonecrop, they are beginning the process of binding together the loose sand or stones.

The Sea Pea, an uncommon perennial pea with big purplish flowers, and deep roots, can grow in the purest shingle on Chesil Bank or on the Suffolk beaches. Another plant with great roots is the Yellow Horned Poppy, that is found on shingle right round the English and Welsh coasts. Its crumpled yellow flowers bloom for five months during the summer, its leaves are hairy and bluish and its seed pods curve over the stones, a good foot long.

Dunes

Higher up the beach the dry sand blowing inshore settles against spikes of Sea Couch grass, and low dunes begin to form. Behind these the stronger Marram grass takes over, its sharp leaves growing through the collecting sand, and the main dunes begin, sometimes building up to a height of sixty feet. A strong wind from an unexpected quarter may blow out the side of a dune and reveal the process of construction within. The whole dune is a mesh of the remains of Marram stems and roots, with a thick living layer at the surface.

Little vegetation can survive on the seaward side of the dune, but on the landward side, protected from the spray, various annual weeds may grow, many in a dwarfed shape and with thickened leaves. Mouse-ear Chickweeds and Whitlow Grasses flower, fruit and die before the summer drought begins, and Ragwort and Dandelions reach down to water with long taproots. These sand-dunes are also the place to find a striking xerophyte – the Sea Holly. This perennial grows about two feet high, with powder-blue flowers and spiny waxen leaves, the whole plant covered with a silvery bloom. Although it grows all along the British coastline, it is becoming scarce in populated districts. Its fleshy root can grow eight feet down through the sand.

Behind these dunes there may be several ranges of fixed or 'grey' dunes. 'Grey' refers to the colour of the lichens that will grow over any fairly stable, bare dunes. The Marram grass is soon crowded out and the flora becomes variable and vivid, coastal flowers mixing with bright little annuals such as Scarlet Pimpernels, Pansies and Speedwells. The alkaline effect of salt and crushed shells among the sand means that such plants as Salad Burnet, Lady's Tresses and Restharrow can grow there. Typical coastal plants among these dunes are the Storksbill, which looks like Herb Robert but is more robust and grows longer seed pods; Buck's-horn Plantain, and pale Burnet Rose.

Further inland the dune flora will vary according to the type of soil. If it is acid there will be heathland and pinewood, and if it is basic there will be grassland and oakwood.

Another type of dune flora is found in the damp valleys that sometimes occur between dunes. These are known as 'dune slacks', and the water beneath the sand is often fresh, so marsh species may grow here, such as Marsh Bedstraw, Grass of Parnassus, Bog Pimpernel and rushes.

Salt marshes

On low, sheltered shores and river estuaries, where muddy silt has collected and the tide is not strong enough to stop the plants taking hold, muddy flats and salt-marshes develop. The flora here is a purely maritime one, and can survive in salt water.

The first plant to grow in a stretch of half-submerged mud is likely to be the Glasswort or Marsh Samphire. This strange, stubby plant is a member of the Goosefoot family, and often forms large colonies that can stretch for miles in the shining mud, and whose colour can vary from yellow to dark green in summer and sometimes bright red in the autumn. There are several species, all with swollen, shiny, jointed stems, no leaves except for scaly leaf bases, and tiny rudimentary flowers sunk in the axils of the branches. Some consist only of a fat twig in the mud, some are prostrate, others form compact little bushes several feet high. Glasswort is edible, and can be eaten fresh in salads or as a pickle.

Silt and rubbish from the tide is trapped round the Glasswort plants, and the level of mud gradually rises. On this slightly higher level, colonies of Annual Sea-blite, another small juicy

Storksbill *Erodium cicutarium* can be distinguished from similar Cranesbills such as Herb Robert by the long beaked fruits that project at angles from among the flowers. There are several species of Storksbills and all grow commonly near the sea in dry sandy places, and as a weed in seaside fields.

Glasswort or Marsh Samphire *Salicornia europaea*. There are many species of Glasswort, some growing prostrate, some in bushes and some as single spikes, and varying in colour from green and yellow to red and orange.

Goosefoot, and Sea Aster, may occur. The Sea Aster has fleshy leaves, but otherwise is similar to the garden Michaelmas Daisy, and flowers in the autumn. Both these plants do not mind some submersion, and will further raise the land level, creating tussocks of vegetation and causing the tide to divide into shallow channels.

The slightly drier conditions on the banks of these channels are ideal for the Sea Purslane, a Goosefoot with wide, pale mealy leaves and yellow flower spikes, which can grow in large groups in the higher levels of salt-marsh on the east coast of England, though it is seldom seen on the west coast or in Scotland. Further silt and rubbish is trapped among its roots and foliage and the hummocks of vegetation build up and come together. This means that the tidal water forms permanent channels and plants such as the Thrift and Sea Lavender which dislike waterlogged mud can grow on the higher level.

Both these plants belong to the same family, and both have a papery calyx which survives into winter making it look like an everlasting flower. The pink flowers of the Thrift or Sea Pink are bunched into a round head on a single tough stalk, and those of the Sea Lavender are purple or mauve, growing along a curved, branching stalk. The Thrift is common everywhere, growing on shingle, cliffs or seaside walls and at high altitudes inland, but the Common Sea Lavender grows mainly on the east coast. Another species, the Remote-flowered Sea Lavender, is sometimes found in western river estuaries, and the Rock Sea Lavender grows locally on western cliffs.

The Common Scurvy Grass inhabits the salt-marsh at this level, and grows right round the British coast and on the sea coasts of northern and western Europe; other species grow in the Arctic and on cliffs and dunes. It is not a grass at all, but a small plant with shiny dark leaves, four white or violet petals set crosswise and round seed pods; dried or distilled, it used to provide Vitamin C for sailors on long voyages, to ward off scurvy.

At the highest level the salt-marsh is often dominated by the Sea Rush, and most herbaceous plants tend to become shaded out. One that sometimes grows in the brackish mud bordering drainage channels is the Marsh Mallow. This is a pale, beautiful plant, with rosy-pink mallow flowers and soft, downy stems and leaves. The root contains starch, albumen, oil, sugar and gelatinous substances, in fact all the ingredients are there for the marshmallow sweet for which the plant was once collected.

The landscape of a salt-marsh may always look the same from a distance, but in fact it is constantly changing. Channels that are scoured by the tide may become blocked with vegetation, and either change direction or form stagnant pools or salt-pans. Shrubby plants, such as the Sea Purslane, may grow right over narrow creeks, which will then flow along underground tunnels. But all this may be destroyed in a moment by a high spring tide with the wind behind it, and the slow accumulation of litter and silt will begin again.

Marsh Mallow *Althaea officinalis*. The soft pink-tinged flowers bloom in late summer in sea dykes and ditches and salt marshes. The whole plant feels like downy velvet and contains gelatinous substances that were used for making marshmallow sweets.

Scurvy Grass *Cochlearia officinalis* belongs to the Cabbage family and the typical four-petalled flowers vary in colour from white to lilac. The globular seed pods are distinctive; the fleshy little leaves are rich in Vitamin C and were used as an anti-scorbutic especially by sailors, for species of Scurvy Grass grow by the sea from the south of England to the Arctic Circle.

Rocks and cliffs

The plants of salt-marshes and dunes play an important part in the way their environment is formed, but on sea cliffs and rocks the vegetation exists as best it can in cracks and crevices and on sheltered ledges. As long as it has some protection from wind and spray, a rich flora can grow, made up of perennial and often halophytic plants with long tough roots for an anchor, and living off moss and debris and the dung of sea birds.

A typical cliff species is the Rock Samphire, a yellow umbellifer with bright green, succulent and aromatic leaves, and a root that can grow three feet into a crack in the cliff face. It grows mainly on the south and west coasts, and is not found in Scotland. The Golden Samphire is not a relation, being a member of the Daisy family. It will grow on shingle and in salt-marshes, but is most common on cliffs, and there it grows a foot tall, with bright yellow flowers similar to those of the inland Fleabane. The Wild Cabbage, the ancestor of our garden varieties, has become a rarity now on southern and western cliffs.

The tough Cresses and Stonecrops that are common on stone walls inland grow on sheltered sea rocks. The largest of the Stonecrops, the Roseroot, is a mountain species, but descends to

ABOVE Hottentot Fig *Carpobrotus edulis* with its pink-mauve flowers flourishes in a sandy soil. It flowers in May–August and has long creeping woody stems.

OPPOSITE Thrift *Armeria maritima* is one of the most familiar sea plants, whose round pink flowerheads and bracts become papery, like everlasting flowers, in the autumn. It grows on cliffs, shingle beaches and on rocks above the tide line, and also, occasionally, on inland mountains. It has sharp little leaves which form a protective cushion. It is growing here with Scurvy Grass and lichen on a cliff face.

sea-level on northern Scottish cliffs, together with several other high-altitude plants.

A native of South Africa, the Hottentot Fig, hangs in great curtains down the cliffs of sheltered coves in Cornwall and Devonshire, and is generally known in this country as 'Mesembryanthemum' or 'Sally-my-handsome'. The curved, keel-shaped leaves are thickly fleshy and the flowers a gaudy pink or yellow; the fig fruits can be eaten but seldom ripen in this country. The Tree Mallow grows in similar places and is a giant of a plant, sometimes eight feet high, with a thick woody stem and pink flowers that bloom in midsummer. There is a rocky bay near Land's End where a Tree Mallow grows on every grassy ledge and heavy masses of Hottentot Fig fall round them, adding a strangely exotic atmosphere to the Cornish scene.

Towards the cliff-top the maritime plants become increasingly mixed with submaritime and inland species, and they also become affected by the type of soil. Cliffs of granite or sandstone will support acid heath plants, and those of chalk and limestone support plants that are common on limy soil.

'Submaritime' is the term generally used for plants that are adapted in some way to coastal conditions and are rarely found inland. The Vernal Squill is submaritime, growing on grassy cliff-tops or sheltered ledges on the western coast. It has delicate, blue, bell-shaped flowers, and grows from a small nut-like bulb. The Autumnal Squill is less common, with flowers of a purplish blue. The Sea Carrot grows frequently on cliff-tops and is different from the common Wild Carrot in that it has fleshy leaves and a convex flowerhead. The heads of the Wild Carrot are flatter, or even concave. Kidney Vetch is common in the short turf of sea cliffs.

Several of the plants described are rare or absent in Scotland, but there is one that only grows on northern cliffs. This is the Lovage, a variety of which is grown in many southern gardens as a potherb, and which grows wild from Northumberland to the Arctic Circle. The leaves are similar to those of Celery, but are a dark and shiny green. It has an umbelliferous flower, and the whole plant is edible and aromatic.

Another group of coastal plants are those that grow in large numbers for a few miles inland, but are seldom found at any distance from the sea. Fennel and Alexanders are included in this group, both being yellow umbellifers and likely to have originally escaped from herb or vegetable gardens. The leaves of the Fennel are finely divided and feathery, with a strong aniseed flavour; the leaves of Alexanders are divided into big shiny leaflets, and the stalks were formerly blanched and eaten like Celery.

Among other plants that seldom grow far from the sea are three species of Storksbill, common weeds in sandy, coastal fields, the Slender-flowered Thistle with clusters of purple flowers and thickly downy leaves and stems, and the Three-cornered Leek that looks like a white Bluebell, has a powerful garlic smell, and grows in the banks of southern seaside lanes.

Acknowledgments

The illustrations on pages 10–13 were painted by Mary French.

Photographs were supplied by or are reproduced by kind permission of the following (numbers refer to page numbers):

A to Z Botanical Collection: Endpapers, 2–3, 9, 12, 29, 37 (*top*), 45, 48 (*top*), 49, 55 (*bottom*), 56, 58 (*top*), 60, 62, 63, 64–5, 66, 69, 78, 80 (*top*), 87 (*top and bottom*), 88 (*bottom*), 90–1, 96, 104, 111 (*top*), 112, 114.

Heather Angel: 24–5, 30, 38–9, 76, 89 (*bottom*), 95, 98–9, 110 (*top*).

Mick Duff: 4–5, 16, 18, 19, 32, 43 (*top*), 48 (*middle*), 50–1, 75, 81 (*top*), 109, 111 (*bottom*), 113.

Ron and Christine Foord: 7, 15, 26, 27, 28 (*top*), 29 (*top*), 31, 35, 41, 44 (*top*), 46, 52, 67, 69, 71, 73, 77, 82, 87, 94, 97, 101, 103 (*bottom*), 106–7, 108, 116.

Angelo Hornak: 6, 8, 14, 20–1, 22, 40 (*top and bottom*), 42, 43, 47, 48 (*bottom*), 55 (*top*), 58–9, 68 (*left*), 70, 74, 93.

Anthony Huxley: 1, 33, 36, 37 (*bottom*), 57, 61, 72, 80 (*bottom*), 86, 102–3, 105, 110 (*bottom*), 115.

Pamla Toler: 84–5.

Soapwort *Saponaria officinalis* was probably imported to this country long ago as a soap substitute, for the boiled leaves will form a lather and remove grease. The gay pink flowers grow from a long green calyx and are found by water and in marshy places.

Bibliography

Herbals their Origin & Evolution: Agnes Arber MA DSc FRS FLS
(Cambridge University Press, 1953)
The Oxford Book of Wild Flowers: Ary & Gregory (Oxford
University Press, 1965)
The Floral Year: L.J.F. Brimble (Macmillan, 1949)
Culpeper's Complete Herbal (Milner & Co, Manchester)
Britain's Structure and Scenery: L. Dudley Stamp (Collins, 1967)
The Broads: E.A. Ellis (Collins, 1965)
The Herbal: John Gerard (1597)
Wild Flowers: John Gilmour & Max Walters (Collins, 1973)
Wild Flowers of the Chalk: John Gilmour (King Penguin, 1947)
A Modern Herbal: M. Grieve (Penguin edition, 1976)
A Dictionary of English Plant Names: Geoffrey Grigson
(Allen Lane, 1974)
The Englishman's Flora: Geoffrey Grigson (Paladin, 1958)
Wild Flowers in Britain: Geoffrey Grigson (Collins, 1948)
Flowers of the Coast: Ian Hepburn (Collins, 1952)
Flowers of the Field: Rev. C.A. Johns BA FLS (London Society
for Promoting Christian Knowledge, 1894)
The Concise British Flora in Colour: W. Keble Martin MA FLS
(Ebury Press & Michael Joseph, 1965)
Wild Flowers of Chalk & Limestone: J.E. Lousley (Collins, 1971)
Food for Free: Richard Mabey (Collins, 1972)
Life in Lakes & Rivers: T.T. Macan & E.B. Worthington
(Collins, 1974)
Collins Pocket Guide to Wild Flowers: McClintock & Fitter
(Collins, 1967)
Grass & Grasslands: Ian Moore (Collins, 1966)
Mountains & Moorlands: W.H. Pearsall (Collins, 1971)
The History of British Vegetation: W. Pennington (English
Universities Press, 1974)
The Useful Plants of Great Britain: C. Pierpoint Johnson
(Robert Hardwick, 1863)
Mountain Flowers: Raven & Walters (Collins, 1956)
Flowers of the Woods: E.J. Salisbury (King Penguin, 1946)
Weeds & Aliens: Sir Edward Salisbury (Collins, 1964)
Life of the Wayside & Woodland: T.R.E. Southwood (Warne, 1963)
Wild Orchids of Britain: V.S. Summerhayes (Collins, 1968)
Britain's Green Mantle: A.G. Tansley, revised by M.C.F. Proctor
(George Allen & Unwin Ltd, 1968)
The Folk-lore of Plants: T.F. Thiselton-Dyer
(Chatto & Windus, 1889)
British Plant Life: W.B. Turrill (Collins, 1948)
The Plant Hunters: Tyler Whittle (Picador, 1970)
Flowers of Marsh & Stream: Iolo A. Williams (King Penguin, 1946)
A Dictionary of the Flowering Plants and Ferns: J.C. Willis
(Cambridge University Press, 1951)
A Prospect of Flowers: Andrew Young (Jonathan Cape, 1946)
A Retrospect of Flowers: Andrew Young (Jonathan Cape, 1950)

Index